Imagination Becomes Reality

Photo by Marc Norberg

REVISED, EXPANDED EDITION

THE TEACHINGS OF MASTER T.T. LIANG

Imagination Becomes Reality

A Complete Guide to the 150 Posture Solo Form

Compiled by Stuart Alve Olson

DRAGON DOOR
PUBLICATIONS

Second Edition (September 1992)

ISBN 0-938045-09-1

First Edition 1986

Printed in the United States of America.

Printed by Gopher State Litho, Minneapolis, Minnesota.

Printed on acid-free paper.

Library of Congress Card Number: 92-73713

THE TEACHINGS OF MASTER T.T. LIANG

IMAGINATION BECOMES REALITY

The Complete Guide to the 150 Posture Solo Form

Compiled by Stuart Alve Olson

All my gratitude goes to Master T.T. Liang for his sharing, teaching and friendship, and for the kind contribution of his calligraphy in Chapter Seven. Without his consent and faith this book could not exist.

Great appreciation goes out to Richard Peterson for his incredible skills and effort with the camera to provide the best T'ai Chi Ch'uan photographs I have ever encountered, along with his patience in having me serve as model — no easy task.

Again, many thanks go the "book wizard", Randy Scholes for his design of the entire book. Words cannot express how greatly his talents are appreciated.

To John Du Cane for both his re-editing of the entire text and his tenacious ability to take care of all the details of such projects. I am forever in his debt.

To my good friend and teacher, Jonathan Russell, for providing the photographs of Master Liang and his introduction to this book. As with Master Liang it would be hard to imagine this book could exist without all his earlier input.

To Mike Urseth for all his data entry and page layout work, patience in putting up with numerous changes and being supportive in these early years of Dragon Door Publications.

—Stuart Olson

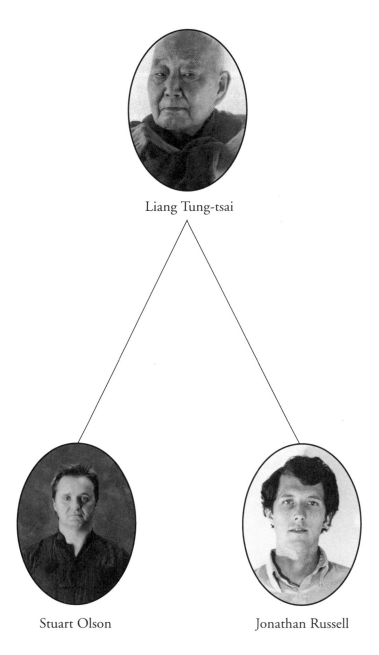

Liang Tung-tsai

Stuart Olson   Jonathan Russell

INTRODUCTION TO FIRST EDITION

When living in Boston, Master Liang decided that he would take an English composition course at the University of Harvard. I was to take him there for his first class. Before setting out I asked him if he knew to what building he was supposed to go. T.T. told me that it had a steeple on top. Anyone who has ever been to Harvard University has undoubtedly noticed the vast number of buildings with white steeples on them. Driving in my car we came upon a yard, a huge lawned area lined with buildings, with a wide sidewalk running down the center. Not being able to locate the right building from the street, T.T. instructed me to drive down the sidewalk in order to find the building and avoid the long walk. At first I refused but T.T. told me not to worry. He would take full responsibility if the Harvard police stopped us. He said they would understand that such an old man should not be allowed to walk such a long distance.

So there we were driving down the sidewalk of the Harvard Yard. Sure enough the Harvard police came racing towards us and pulled my car over. Just as this happened T.T. jumped from the car, stood back, pointed at me and in a accusatorial manner yelled, "Arrest that man! He's a crazy man and should be put in jail!" He then walked down the sidewalk to the street to catch a bus home, leaving me the task of dealing with the police. He laughed for days after about how startled, confused and afraid I was during the whole ordeal.

Arrest that man! He's a crazy man and should be put in jail!

With Master Liang you never know when he may catch you with one of his playful intimidating pranks, which is just like his skill in pushing-hands practice; you can never tell when a push is coming either.

The reason for Liang's playful intimidation is not just to test your patience or ability to yield, rather its significance goes to the very root of the internal aspect of T'ai Chi, "abiding by the tan-tien". The essence of any practice of the internal arts (*nei kung*) is centered on this abiding by the tan-tien. In fact you cannot acquire such skills as root (central equilibrium), neutralization, counter-attack, nourishing the three treasures (ching, ch'i and shen), interpretation of energy and sticky energy without adhering to this rule. They all have their source through abiding by this tan-tien. So Liang's playful intimidation is no more than a test to see if you can keep the ch'i down by not overreacting to any situation—a kind of verbal push-hands. Those who study T'ai Chi Ch'uan hear and read repeatedly the words, "sink your ch'i," "learn how to lose," "yield," "non-resistance," and "abide by the tan-tien." It is these principles that Liang constantly attacks and tests.

Abiding by the tan-tien can only be done through use of the "imagination." To the novice, no tan-tien can be either observed or felt, therefore one must first imagine this and gradually it will become real after long, mindful practice.

During the years I studied and helped teach T'ai Chi with Master Liang, he would constantly admonish his students to use their imagination so that eventually it would become a reality. Over and over again I would hear him say things like:

"When you are a beginner you should pretend that you have the skill of a great master and your progress will be very rapid."

"You should pretend that your body is floating in water so that you feel a

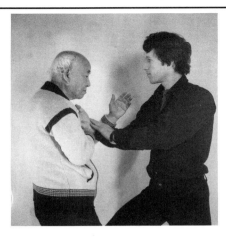

Jonathan Russell
and T.T. Liang

It is a secret that protects itself from being discovered because it is so simple.

slight pressure against your every movement."

"You imagine that as you push, your energy is directed by the mind and follows your intent."

"You imagine that your center of gravity falls below the floor and you become firmly rooted. "

"You imagine . . . imagine . . . imagine."

T'ai Chi Ch'uan is truly a form of imagination. From working with Liang it becomes clear that ten percent of T'ai Chi is what you can see (the external movements) and the other ninety percent is what you cannot see, that is, the internal realm, the area that can be stimulated by correctly guiding your imagination. Real progress comes not from learning more and more, new and beautiful forms, (although T.T. is always dangling a new form that we don't know yet in front of our eyes) but from working with the most difficult and intangible area—the imagination.

Not surprisingly it is also the most difficult aspect for students to comprehend and is the secret of T'ai Chi. It is a secret that protects itself from being discovered because it is so simple. Most students feel that they have to acquire new knowledge, new techniques, when the tool that will really help them progress is with them all the time—their imagination. If this can be mastered, the internal realm of T'ai Chi Ch'uan will follow.

In the case of Stuart Olson, who is the only student to live with Master Liang for such an extended period of time, he has truly learned how to make his imagination become a reality, not only with his T'ai Chi but with his dreams as well. Two years ago he described to me his idea for a publishing house, and that he wished to make it become a reality. This sounded great to me but I thought to myself that it was, as Liang often says, "a bounced check." To my amazement what was in Stuart's imagination really has become a reality. Now if some of the other ideas in his head also become real—watch out! I for one definitely want to witness the realities of his imagination.

Jonathan Russell, Senior Student
Winter, 1985

INTRODUCTION TO SECOND EDITION

Nearly thirteen years ago I became fascinated with the art of T'ai Chi Ch'uan. At that time I had no conception that my life would become so deeply involved with it. At first it was a mere fascination with its mystical aspects. Later it became not only a means of livelihood but a way of life. Between teaching, writing and practicing T'ai Chi, I have found much truth in Master T. T. Liang's words, "At first I took T'ai Chi as a hobby to improve my health, gradually I became addicted to it and could not get rid of it." The same has been true for me.

I no longer look to T'ai Chi for any mystical experiences or wisdom, rather, my approach is that of searching for the more practical and humanistic aspects of this art.

T'ai Chi, aside from all the supernatural tales surrounding it, is really nothing more than a basis for becoming a centered and aware human being. In my opinion, man learns little about himself or the spiritual realms when he is constantly looking outside his or her "self" . T'ai Chi, like Zen, is only concerned with the here and now. Of course certain abilities, which the unlearned grasp as mystical feats, are cultivated within T'ai Chi, but they are nothing more than natural, inherent skills existing in everyone. Because of our tension, fears and bad habits these skills remain hidden, potential rather than kinetic. T'ai Chi helps draw them out.

T'ai Chi, like Zen, is only concerned with the here and now.

By becoming centered not only in the body but mind, developing awareness and sensitivity and ingraining the principles of T'ai Chi into your actions and thoughts, it is possible to understand the "here and now" and experience the so-called mystical skills of T'ai Chi. It all boils down to one thing, becoming a better human being by striving to make use of your full potential in the most efficient way possible. From this we can come to understand why T'ai Chi can encompass not only health, martial art and mental accomplishment, but immortality as well.

For over five years I lived and studied with the great T'ai Chi master, T. T. Liang, who is a living example of the efficacy of this profound and subtle art. His teaching is always practical, never mystical—indeed this is what most erroneously conceive as his mystical side. His simplicity is difficult to comprehend by those who live such complicated lives, who refuse to yield with life and who are always on the defensive. Master Liang is like a willow tree wherein the branches yield to everything, yet the trunk remains rooted and stable. Those of us who have been fortunate enough to study with him understand this about him more than anything else.

The title of this book *Imagination Becomes Reality*, reflects the underlying teaching of Master T. T. Liang. The entire condition for attaining the skills of T'ai Chi Ch'uan rests within your imagination. T'ai Chi is a matter of "mind-intent" rather than of gross physical skills that emphasize external muscular force. As Master Liang often states, "When practicing T'ai Chi you must presume an opponent is in front of you. Gradually through continued practice the intrinsic energy, the ch'i and the technique will come out spontaneously in time of emergency." If caught unawares by an attack you will automatically react,

T.T. with "young man" Stuart Olson.

I only remember consciously doing a few postures, after that, just paradise.

with no time to think of a trained response. Hence, he summarizes this in the statement "imagination becomes reality."

Many years ago while I was living with Master Liang I asked him about an experience he related in his book, *T'ai Chi Ch'uan for Health and Self-Defense,* in which he states, "After sufficient practice, you will master the 150 postures so thoroughly that you will forget the rhythm, the movement, even yourself — although you are proceeding as usual. At this stage, you are in a trance; your five attributes (form, perception, consciousness, action and knowledge) are all empty — this is *tranquility in motion, motion in tranquility.* When you finish and come to the end of the postures suddenly you are back. Where have I been? What have I been doing? I don't know and I don't remember. This is complete relaxation of body and mind lasting thirty minutes. For thirty minutes I really was in another world. It was an ideal world, peaceful and quiet. After the total relaxation of body and mind for this thirty minutes in the ideal world, I return to this one."

He then retorted, "Young man, this is a most incredible state, unbelievable! When this experience first occurred I was so surprised. A couple of my good teachers told me that if I exercised my imagination within my practice I could achieve incredible states, but I was stubborn for many years and did not believe it. But now it has become a reality for me. I only remember consciously doing a few postures, after that, just paradise. This is why I say T'ai Chi Ch'uan is so profound and abstruse. However if you do not devote yourself studiously for a long period you can only acquire the skin, not the marrow."

T.T. added that to truly master T'ai Chi Ch'uan you need to study good books and the classics, learn from good teachers, then apply it to your practice through imagination, then gradually it will become a reality.

Imagination is at the very heart of T'ai Chi Ch'uan, just as it is the source for all our aspirations, inventions, religions and cultures. Creation begins with imagination. Nothing real comes into being without the inception of imagination. We are, as human beings, a creation of imagination. Our lives are a direct result of our ability to imagine.

Some might argue that karma is the source of our existence, not imagination. Karma however is like the Chinese philosophical idea of *Hsien T'ien Ch'i* (Before Heaven Ch'i), meaning, the ch'i we inherited from our parents, ancestors and previous incarnations. *Hou T'ien Ch'i* (After Heaven Ch'i) is what we accumulate as a result of our conduct and practices. This Hou T'ien Ch'i is rooted in imagination. You can find no practice, no faith, no philosophy which does not first incorporate imagination.

The Chinese word for imagination is *hsiang* (想) which expresses the ideas of, interdependent mind, to see the mind, and the form or symbol of the mind. The primitive meaning of the topmost radical (also pronounced hsiang) is to watch or look (目) from behind a tree (木). From this came the ideas of examining and inspecting. This looking from behind a tree was used in relation to someone in a forest becoming aware and alert of wild beasts, sounds and directions. So the fuller meaning here is something more like observing through awareness. By placing *hsin* (心) underneath hsiang the idea is clear, watchful awareness of the mind. To the Chinese the imagination is mind, as all things come from the mind. Imagination is not a matter of conjuring up images. The images are the mind.

In English we normally give two meanings to the word:

1) The power to reproduce images stored in the memory or to create new images through suggestion or by recombining former experiences.

2) To form mental images of things not present or empirically real to the senses.

In the Chinese view of such things as imagination, thought, will and intent, there must be an understanding of hsin (mind and/or heart). To the Chinese there is no separation of these two functions. For example, the Buddhist would describe hsin (心) as a hook (ㄴ) and the three dots as representations either of *greed, anger* and *ignorance* in the unenlightened state, or of *charity, compassion* and *wisdom* in the enlightened state. The hook then represents that which renders them interdependent. With greed there will also be anger and ignorance; with charity there will be compassion and wisdom.

The Taoist views the three dots as *sun, moon* and *stars; heaven, earth* and *man*, or; *ching, ch'i* and *shen*, all of which are interdependent. For example, when the mind attaches itself to one thing it hooks the counterparts and so the heart/mind is affected either positively or negatively.

With this understood, we can proceed to the concept of *i* (mind-intent). The character consists of three radicals. The topmost is *li* (立) which means to establish or fix. The middle radical is *jih* (日) the sun, and the bottom character again is *hsin* (心) the mind/heart. The idea here is a symbol expressing "establishing brightness of mind". To the Chinese, mind-intent is therefore a mind/heart that is clear and focused.

Hsiang is the bridge between hsin and i, or the imagination process is the cohesive factor which can unite the rational thinking mind with the mind-intent.

Chen Kung, in my translation, *Cultivating the Ch'i*, states: "Some have said that mind-intent is no other than the mind (rational thinking) or that the mind is no other than the mind-intent. But truly there is both a mind and mind-intent; they are two separate things and should be thought of as such. The master of the mind is the mind-intent. The mind acts as only an assistant to the mind-intent. When the mind moves, it does so because of the mind-intent; when the mind-intent arises the ch'i will follow."

My footnote on mind-intent from the above work is worth mentioning here:

"In the practice of T'ai Chi Ch'uan the function of the mind-intent, or will, is both transcendental and intrinsically connected with ch'i. Mind-intent is nei-

To the Chinese the imagination is mind, as all things come from the mind.

ther a conditioned response nor an unconscious reaction. It is a reaction founded in awareness, intuition and sensitivity. However, mind-intent is "conditioned" in that it is developed over a long period of time through practice of the various T'ai Chi Ch'uan exercises. The mind-intent is also "unconscious" in that the rational thinking mind is not used.

The problem in defining the mind-intent is an empirical one in that you must first be truly capable of sinking the ch'i into tan-tien, which then strengthens the vitality of mind-intent, which in turn will affect the mind, producing tranquility. So without initiating the use of mind-intent, however vague at first, in order to sink the ch'i into the tan-tien, the mind-intent cannot be made strong enough for you to truly realize the difference between mind-intent and mind."

*I*n T'ai Chi Ch'uan the yang energy only occurs for an instant, like energy coming off the tip of a whip.

When practicing T'ai Chi Ch'uan we are told to presume that there is an opponent in front of us and to imagine that we apply the techniques masterfully. After a long period of practicing this way we will achieve a functional mastery of T'ai Chi Ch'uan. This is true, but it is only half the story and only hints at mind-intent's full extent.

First, when presuming an opponent, you must imagine that you do not injure the opponent, that this is playful. There should be nothing violent about your imagining. Otherwise you will only succeed in producing more tension, both mentally and physically. In actual sparring you will then be unable to relax (*sung*); you will not be sensitive and alert.

Secondly, you must imagine that all your motions of neutralizing and seizing are soft and gentle, yet precise and efficient. Relax does not become collapse. Softness does not transform into dullness.

Learn from a competent teacher, so that you know the precise use of every movement of every posture, otherwise your mind-intent will be broken. You must also know precisely at what point you are releasing energy in each posture and how to root. In T'ai Chi Ch'uan the yang energy only occurs for an instant, like energy coming off the tip of a whip, which then immediately returns to yin. You must also imagine that you are always stepping into and on the opponent's center, taking his space and making him defective, finding the line of attack and simultaneously affecting the upper, middle and lower regions of his body.

Thirdly, pay no attention to the breath, only to your mind-intent (the imagination process). In The Mental Elucidation of the Thirteen Kinetic Postures it says, "The mind-intent of your entire being must be in the spirit of vitality (shen), not in the breath (and ch'i); if it is in the breath (and ch'i) the result will be stagnation. You will have ch'i without strength."

The breath and ch'i will come of themselves if you pay attention to the mind-intent of your technique and attempt to keep them internalized. For example, "hollowing the chest" is not something you perform physically, but rather an internal letting go of any tension and protrusion there might be. All the internal principles are like this.

When you are able to apply these three factors of presuming (imagining) an opponent, the mind-intent will begin to take over your movement. This does take a long period of correct practice. From acquiring a functional mind-intent you can then begin to know what is meant by shen (spirit or spirit of vitality).

Now the imagination has become the reality, rather than an imagination *hoping* to become reality.

Another method of applying the imagination to T'ai Chi Ch'uan practice is to imagine some sort of resistance while you move, as though you were swimming in water or moving in a heavy thick air. This method is quite good, but is solely aimed at the ch'i-kung aspect of T'ai Chi Ch'uan. It focuses on the accumulation of ch'i rather than the intrinsic (*chin*) energy used in practical applications of the art.

In using this imagined resistance method you should reach a state, relatively quickly, of experiencing incredible heaviness or of a surging of energy. The heaviness is the response of becoming yin, a point where the yang in your body is waning. You might feel a vibration throughout your body or just a heaviness which makes you feel as though you cannot continue moving. This is completely natural and you need only to keep practicing and go beyond it. Gradually as you learn to sink this energy down to the bottom of your feet the sensation will be of lightness and nimbleness.

The surging sensation is the ch'i stimulating circulation of the blood. At first it is an unconscious experience, meaning it is not something you consciously control. Gradually over a long period of practice the mind-intent will control it. It is important not to become attached to these experiences, no matter the method or sensation. Just continue to practice. Attachment will lead to stagnation of both mind and mind-intent.

In conclusion, the use of your imaginary faculties are paramount to the mastery of T'ai Chi Ch'uan. Principles and techniques are only the branches of the art. Imagination leads you to the trunk and roots, which are mind-intent and spirit.

Stuart Alve Olson
Summer, 1992

Imagination leads you to the trunk and roots, which are mind-intent and spirit.

A BIOGRAPHY OF MASTER T.T. LIANG

Tung-tsai Liang was born in Hobei province, China, in 1900. His father was a merchant and his mother a very devout lay Buddhist. After college, Liang joined the maritime customs service at age twenty-four and served as a high ranking official for over 30 years. After the beginning of World War II he was transferred to Taiwan where he retired.

Since his move to the United States in 1963, Liang estimates that he has taught T'ai Chi Ch'uan to well over 3,000 students. He has taught in such places as China, Taiwan, England, New York, Boston, Minnesota, Florida and California.

He and his teacher, Professor Cheng Man-ch'ing, were the first official demonstrators of T'ai Chi Ch'uan in America, doing so at the United Nations in New York. Liang was Professor Cheng's first and eldest disciple, with more than twenty years service as his student. This earned him the title of Ta Shih Hsiung (Chief Disciple). While in New York at the United Nations, Liang served as both Professor Cheng's interpreter and teaching assistant. Later on Liang taught on his own at the United Nations and many well known colleges including Boston College, Harvard University, Amherst, Springfield, Tufts, and Cumbres.

Because of his many location changes while serving as a customs official, Liang was able to meet many martial arts masters and practitioners. He studied under 15 prominent masters in all. The most notable were: Professor Cheng, Yuan Tao, Li Shou-chen, Hsiung Yang-ho, Han Ching-tang, and Chang Tsun-feng. He studied such arts as: T'ai Chi Ch'uan, Hsing-I Ch'uan, Pa Kua Chang, Tang Lang Ch'uan (Praying Mantis), Shaolin Ch'uan, Chin Na and many related weapons. Some of Liang's more notable classmates were William C. C. Chen and Benjamin Lo.

Liang actually began his study of the martial arts at age twelve, but did not practice T'ai Chi Ch'uan seriously until an illness at age forty almost took his life. Suffering from both a liver infection and pneumonia, he was given only two months to live. In order to save his own life he undertook vigorous T'ai Chi Ch'uan practice. As he explains in his book, *T'ai Chi Ch'uan for Health and Self-Defense,* "At first I took up T'ai Chi Ch'uan as a hobby; gradually I became addicted to it; now I can no longer get rid of it. I must keep on practicing for my whole life—it is the only way to preserve health."

Within two years Liang's health had greatly improved. Now at age ninety-two he is a living example of the benefits of serious T'ai Chi Ch'uan practice. Even after 52 years of daily practice, his enthusiasm for the art is still strong.

I must keep on practicing for my whole life—it is the only way to preserve health.

THE TEACHINGS OF MASTER T.T. LIANG

CHAPTER ONE
INTERVIEWS WITH MASTER T. T. LIANG

The Origins of T'ai Chi Ch'uan

What is T'ai Chi Ch'uan and how was it created?

First of all, T'ai Chi Ch'uan is commonly called just "T'ai Chi." It is an ancient form of classical dance created about seven hundred years ago by Chang San-feng, a Taoist priest of the Sung dynasty.

I will tell you how Chang San-feng created the circular version of T'ai Chi Ch'uan. Chang was a Taoist who travelled to many places by himself. He eventually arrived on Wu-Tang Mountain, in Hupei province, to study the old T'ai Chi classics and the original thirteen postures of T'ai Chi Ch'uan as practiced by the Taoists living there.

One day, while on Wu-Tang Mountain, he was reading the classics and heard a noise outside his hut. He looked outside and saw a magpie fighting with a snake on the ground. The bird would fly down from the tree and attempt to bite the snake. The snake could do little but by only moving his head, he could neutralize and avoid the attacks. He simply yielded, turning from side to side, to avoid the biting of the bird.

After a little while, the bird flew back up into the tree, being too tired perhaps. Later on the bird again flew down to attack the snake. This time the bird tried using its wings to strike the snake. The snake again yielded, by turning from one side to another, neutralizing with his head as before. After many attempts, the bird could still not bite the snake. Both had become extremely tired, so they quit fighting and the bird flew away.

*H*e simply yielded, turning from side to side, to avoid the biting of the bird.

From this incident, Chang San-feng began to develop the method of T'ai Chi. He adopted the hard and soft, combining them according to the T'ai Chi principles of the original thirteen postures and variations of yin and yang energy. He created what we now know as T'ai Chi Ch'uan, the round form. This is why it is called "tranquility in motion, motion in tranquility."

How did T'ai Chi Ch'uan get handed down from Chang San-feng to the present day?

Chang San-feng handed down his art to his disciple, Wang Chung-yueh. Wang wrote additional classics to preserve the art. This helped promote T'ai Chi. Now we have something upon which to base our practice. Gradually the art moved to the Chen family, who hid it from outsiders for over three hundred years. After several generations it came to the Yang family. Now we may talk about the Yang family and Yang Lu-chan, the founder of the Yang style of T'ai Chi.

Yang Lu-chan was born in Hobei province. When he was still a young man, he travelled to Honan province. This occurred over one hundred years ago. The Chen family lived in Honan province and Yang journeyed there to learn T'ai Chi from the head of the family, Chen Chang-hsing. Chen was very skilled in T'ai Chi and had a good reputation.

At this time, however, the Chen family would teach only their own relatives.

Yang Lu-chan definitely wanted to learn T'ai Chi from Chen but he knew he would receive little instruction if he just asked to be taught. Yang was very clever and pretended to be deaf and dumb. When he arrived at the village, the Chens felt sorry for him and gave him a job as a servant. Yang secretly watched Chen Chang-hsing teaching his students every day. Eventually Chen discovered Yang spying on him and realized that he was not deaf and dumb. Yang Lu-chan then told him the whole story and asked Chen to teach him his art. Chen agreed, showed him a little bit and liked that Yang caught on so quickly. From then on Chen Chang-hsing taught Yang Lu-chan everything he knew about T'ai Chi.

After about two years Yang had acquired all of Chen's art. One day Chen Chang-hsing called together his immediate family and relatives. He told them that a student named Yang Lu-chan had learned his entire art. He said that he had wanted to hand down his art to his family but that they were not able to learn it. He said Yang Lu-chan had managed to learn the art and was now leaving.

After leaving the Chen family village, Yang Lu-chan went back to Beijing to teach the royal family and make T'ai Chi available to the public. In the palace he taught the princes, princesses and priests. Through time he taught far and wide and his skill became well known. No one could defeat him and he became known as "Yang the Unbeatable". He was the best of all.

Yang Lu-chan had three sons. The eldest, named Yang Feng-hou, died young. The second son was Yang Pan-hou and the third was called Yang Chien-hou. These two sons did not learn their father's entire art. It is not that they weren't skillful for they were great T'ai Chi masters. Pan-hou practiced all of the time. In fact all he did was practice, his whole life through. Pan-hou reached the stage where if he stretched out his hand, he would hurt you, so few dared to learn from him.

Yang Chien-hou also had three sons, of which the second died young. Both Yang Shao-hou and Yang Cheng-fu, like their grandfather and father, practiced T'ai Chi and mastered the art. There are many stories of combat concerning these two sons because they liked to fight. Yang Cheng-fu, when young, didn't like to practice T'ai Chi and didn't really learn it from his father until he was older. It wasn't until his father had died that Yang Cheng-fu regretted not having had the art handed down to him. He wished to hand it down to his children. To make up for this loss, Yang Cheng-fu practiced very hard every day and learned as much as he could from the other family members. Eventually he became an expert.

Afterwards Cheng-fu changed the style to be even softer than that of his grandfather and father. His form looked soft but internally it was very powerful. That is why it was often said that his arms felt like iron bars wrapped in cotton. He was very kind and his temper very mild, so many students came to learn from him.

Yang Cheng-fu had four sons. The eldest was named Chen-ming; the second, Chen-chi; the third son was called Chen-to and the fourth, Chen-kou.

From this lineage the Yang style of T'ai Chi has progressed and remained popular. Of course the best one was the grandfather, Yang Lu-chan. He handed

*N*o one could defeat him and he became known as "Yang the Unbeatable".

Chang San-feng observes the snake and bird. (Painting by T.T. Liang)

down his art to his sons but they never reached his level of skill. The last generation, now living in Hong Kong, have gradually made the style more and more popular, even in the United States. In my opinion the Yang style of T'ai Chi Ch'uan is the best.

You stated that T'ai Chi Ch'uan has a Taoist origin. What does the Taoist philosophy of Lao Tzu and T'ai Chi Ch'uan have in common?

Everything you do in T'ai Chi Ch'uan has an equivalent in the philosophy of Lao Tzu or simply Taoism in general. In my book, **T'ai Chi Ch'uan for Health and Self Defense**, I discuss at length the similarities between Lao Tzu's Taoism and the T'ai Chi classics. I will say, however, that the greatest similarity occurs at the highest stage of T'ai Chi practice, that of immortality. The final goal of both T'ai Chi and Taoism is immortality.

*T*he final goal of both T'ai Chi and Taoism is immortality.

Chang San-feng, a Taoist, created T'ai Chi Ch'uan. He later became an immortal through his practice of T'ai Chi so it is said that T'ai Chi Ch'uan is a Taoist method for attaining immortality.

The yin and yang symbol represents T'ai Chi. Why is this so?

Yin and yang are in the T'ai Chi Tu (symbol) with one half being yin and the other half being yang. Yang is the substantial and yin the insubstantial. Yang is hard and yin is soft. All of T'ai Chi is based on this yin and yang principle.

The principle relates to T'ai Chi Ch'uan with regards to its roundness. T'ai Chi must have roundness in its form. It must be practiced with circularity and contain yin and yang within.

The postures must be circular and not angular. This is especially true for the beginner. The circles should be large to begin with and gradually condensed into small ones. After you have acquired the art, the small circles become invisible.

Even the body has yin and yang aspects to it. When learning T'ai Chi you must realize the practical use of the postures. To learn this it is necessary to know the opponent, that is, where the yin and yang areas are on his body. A push will be effective if done on the yang part but you will not be able to push him over if you strike his yin area.

Yin and yang can be found throughout T'ai Chi with everything performed in circles. So the T'ai Chi Tu well represents the art.

Why should we practice T'ai Chi Ch'uan and what is the learning process?

The fundamental principles for learning T'ai Chi fall into four categories: health, self-defense, mental accomplishment and immortality.

First, we must discuss *health*. In the T'ai Chi classics it says, "When the lowest vertebrae are plumb erect, the spirit of vitality reaches the top of the head." When the top of the head feels as if it is suspended from above, the whole body will be light and nimble. This is the way to strengthen the spine and by doing this, you not only strengthen the internal organs but the brain itself.

Lao Tzu sightseeing. (Painting by T.T. Liang)

The T'ai Chi classics also state that the "ch'i must be stimulated." The ch'i is an inherent oxygen in the blood necessary for stamina and vitality. The stimulation of the ch'i can be compared to the action of wind on the smooth surface of a lake. As the wind moves across the water, it creates waves, blowing them upward and downward in a systematic order of troughs and crests.

The ch'i, latent in the body, is not sufficiently forceful in itself to increase the flow of blood but if persistently stimulated it can produce heat. This can be very effective in circulating the blood evenly throughout the entire body. The same principle is illustrated by the conversion of water into steam. The invisible power latent in water is made active enough to drive the piston of a powerful engine.

To practice T'ai Chi Ch'uan, it is best to rise early and practice outdoors. To do this it is necessary to keep away from the alcoholic, drug addict and gambler. You must get rid of bad habits. Assimilate the new and let go of the old.

I introduced the system of using beats so that the postures could be practiced slowly to music. By doing the exercises effortlessly and evenly coordination is created between the mind and the body. "Early to bed, early to rise, along with a round of T'ai Chi morning and evening, makes a man or woman, healthy, wealthy and wise!" This is for health.

After you have acquired good health, you may seek the *self-defense* aspects. By practicing the one hundred and fifty postures of T'ai Chi you will develop central equilibrium, that is a firm rooting of the feet. From pushing-hands, you will learn yielding and neutralizing attacks. Practicing the one hundred and seventy-eight posture two-person dance is also necessary. This will develop intrinsic energy in the sinews and tendons because you will learn to use the whole body as one unit. A strike with only the hand will make the body become tense. This is not only ineffective for functional use but harmful to your health. Various energies will be developed over a period of time and this will aid in acquiring the self defense aspect of the art.

The third stage is *mental accomplishment*. After attaining good health and

The stimulation of the ch'i can be compared to the action of wind on the smooth surface of a lake.

acquiring the techniques of self-defense it is necessary to realize mental accomplishment. To accomplish T'ai Chi physically and technically is relatively easy in comparison to attaining it mentally. From my more than forty years of experience, learning and practicing T'ai Chi, I have formulated ten theorems for my daily guiding principles to help me to know how to deal with people and myself. The principles are as follows:

1. *No one can be perfect. Take what is good and discard what is bad.*

2. *If I believe entirely in books, it is better not to read books. If I rely entirely on teachers, it is better not to have teachers.*

3. *To remove a mountain is easy but to change a man's temperament is more difficult.*

4. *If there is anything wrong with me, I do not blame others, I only blame myself.*

5. *If I want to live longer I must learn T'ai Chi and accomplish it both physically and mentally. To accomplish it mentally is much more difficult.*

6. *I must learn how to yield, be tactful, not be aggressive, to lose (small loss, small gain, great loss, great gain) and how not to take advantage of others. I must also learn how to give for the more one gives the more one will have.*

7. *Life begins at seventy. Everything is beautiful! Health is a matter of utmost importance and all of the rest is secondary. Now I must find out how to enjoy excellent health in my whole life and discover the way to immortality.*

8. *Make one thousand friends but not one enemy.*

9. *One must practice what one preaches, otherwise, it is empty talk or a bounced check.*

10. *To conceal the faults of others and praise their good points is the best policy.*

By learning and practicing T'ai Chi and by following the ten theorems as mentioned above, your hot temper will gradually become mild. Hatred, jealousy, anger and all depraved thoughts will disappear. Your evil temperament will be reformed, leaving evil to follow the good. Your mind will become upright and pure.

When you reach the age of seventy, you will enjoy a happy, peaceful and quiet life. At that age you will realize that fame, wealth, authority and honor are all dust. You will then purify your mind and lessen your desires so that you can fully enjoy your life and appreciate nature. That is why I say that life begins at seventy. The world is beautiful.

Now we come to the last stage, that of *immortality*. The ultimate goal for learning and practicing T'ai Chi is to become an immortal. Let me recount an old belief!

When Chang San-feng had sat in meditation on Wu-Tang Mountain for nine years, he still could not obtain his final goal, that of becoming an immortal. One day he got up from his meditation and began practicing the posture "Step Back To Chase The Monkey Away." After less than thirty minutes he suddenly felt that all of the joints in his body had opened wide. His spirit immediately took flight to another world, paradise and he became an immortal.

Ordinarily the two bones of the buttocks are pinched and the ch'i cannot sink downward. When Chang San-feng practiced this posture he put one foot behind, with the feet parallel and the toes pointing directly ahead. His stance was such that the distance between his two legs was of shoulder-width. This

Life begins at seventy. Everything is beautiful!

allowed the ch'i to sink downward to the legs and into the "bubbling-well" points on the soles of the feet, thereby pushing the blood throughout the entire body without hindrance. This is how Chang San-feng finally reached his goal and became an immortal.

The principles and theories of T'ai Chi are so profound and abstruse and the applications so subtle and ingenious that it is important to find the correct method of learning and practicing. If what is learned is not quite accurate and correct, then your ability may be severely handicapped. The fundamental use of T'ai Chi will be lost and it will be useless to talk about mental accomplishment and the way to immortality.

Whether it is possible to achieve immortality by learning and practicing T'ai Chi, is not the main concern. The greatest hope is that of reaching one hundred years of age or more. This is the highest level of longevity.

Nevertheless, a person's life and death are predetermined. Wealth, poverty, fame and honor are in the hands of heaven. I strongly believe in cause and effect. We must live virtuously, enjoy life, appreciate nature and wait for our final allotment so that we have not spent the best days of our life in vain.

His spirit imme- diately took flight to another world, paradise and he became an immortal.

Would you list the complete set of T'ai Chi Ch'uan?
If you wish to study T'ai Chi for health and self-defense it is necessary to learn the entire set of T'ai Chi Ch'uan. The complete set is as follows:
1. T'ai Chi solo dance (right and left styles with 150 postures in each style).
2. Pushing-Hands (active steps in fixed position, 8 movements).
3. Ta Lu (3 sets, total of 26 postures).
4. T'ai Chi Two-Person Dance (178 postures).
5. T'ai Chi Double-Edged Sword Dance (right and left styles, 60 postures in each).
6. T'ai Chi Sword Fencing (46 postures).
7. T'ai Chi Knife Dance (right and left styles, 32 postures in each).
8. T'ai Chi Knife Fencing (24 postures).
9. T'ai Chi Staff Solo Exercise (3 movements).
10. T'ai Chi Staff Fencing (8 postures).
All of these exercises can be practiced to music. *NO*

Personal Experiences

Why did you take up T'ai Chi Ch'uan?
When I was a young man I practiced many hard styles like karate, judo and Chinese Shaolin kung-fu. I also played many sports such as soccer, basketball and tennis. I began working with the Chinese Maritime Customs in my early twenties. Eventually I reached the high position of Chief Tide Surveyor. During this time, I dissipated and drank too much and at the age of forty-five I became very sick. I was committed to a hospital for more than fifty days. During this time I nearly died.

After recovering and leaving the hospital I was still weak to the point where I could no longer do the hard styles of kung-fu. I thought that the best way for me to regain my health would be to learn T'ai Chi Ch'uan. I did so and eventu-

**Chang San-feng.
(Painting by T.T.
Liang)**

ally learned from almost fifteen teachers. The best of them all, in my opinion, was Professor Cheng Man-ch'ing. I have, to the most extent, adopted his method of performing the T'ai Chi Ch'uan exercise.

It took me ten years to regain my health. After that I continued to practice. Now I am over eighty-five years of age and enjoy perfect health. If not for T'ai Chi Ch'uan I can easily say that my life would have ended forty years ago. Of all of the forms of exercise I consider T'ai Chi Ch'uan the best. It saved my life and that is why I strongly advocate that everyone take up this exercise so that they may also enjoy good health.

If not for T'ai Chi Ch'uan I can easily say that my life would have ended forty years ago.

How has T'ai Chi affected you personally?

T'ai Chi has affected me a great deal. When I was young I had a very bad temper which got me into a lot of trouble. I was always ready to fight and generally did a lot of notorious things. Even when I joined the Maritime Customs Service, with a good position and pay, I would get into a lot of trouble. Twice I was disrated, meaning my pay would not be increased. I didn't care. When I reached the highest position that I could, I thought of myself as a real authority. At this time I had bodyguards and when I gave an order, it had to be carried out immediately. I did not believe in anyone but myself. I became very sick during this time and was committed to a hospital. When I was released I took up T'ai Chi.

I have been learning and practicing T'ai Chi for more than forty years now. After the first five years I thought that I knew everything and started to criticize this man and that man as being unskilled. So actually in all this time my attitude hadn't really changed. I began to think that only I was any good. After another ten years of learning and practicing, I began to realize that I knew only a little about T'ai Chi and life in general. Instead of criticizing others, I started to criticize myself because l realized that I was not qualified to judge with my smattering of knowledge. Besides, I had no time to criticize others because I had to practice and painstakingly learn from teachers, books and the T'ai Chi classics.

The more I learned, the less I felt that I knew. The theory and philosophy of T'ai Chi are so profound and abstruse and the functional use so subtle and ingenious, that I felt I must continue studying and practicing T'ai Chi forever. I am still of that opinion. It is the only way to improve and better myself. So, yes, I can say that T'ai Chi has, indeed, affected me a great deal.

The Practice

What is it that you do in this exercise?

The essence of T'ai Chi is to relax, sink all of the weight downward and sink the ch'i into the tan-tien. The whole body must be entirely relaxed. This is very beneficial for health.

What is the difference between T'ai Chi Ch'uan and other popular forms of exercises in terms of its advantages?

T'ai Chi is different from yoga and other forms of exercise. It is not only excellent for your health but develops self-defense skills as well.

Yoga is good, without question and jogging is fine too. Most of the common forms of exercise, however, are beneficial only when the person is young. At an older age, exercises like jogging can lose their health benefits. Jogging can be hard on the joints and place undue stress on the heart.

T'ai Chi, however, is beneficial, no matter what age it is practiced. Whether young, old, male or female, it is an exercise that promotes good health. Also, practice after a period of time will develop self-defense skills. Jogging and yoga will not teach this.

How can these slow, dance-like movements be used for health?

That is an interesting question. Slow motion is good for health because first of all by practicing slowly the ch'i can sink to the tan-tien. This energy, ch'i, will gradually penetrate into the sinews and tendons making the bones very resilient. Sinking the ch'i will also allow the blood to circulate freely throughout the entire body. This is very important for your health.

T'ai Chi Ch'uan, as a martial art, emphasizes relaxation. If the body is tense, the ch'i will rise up impeding blood circulation. This is common with the hard styles like kung-fu and karate. These arts involve using external, muscular force, called *li* which is issued from the bone. By striking this way it is possible to hurt yourself and the resulting tension is not beneficial.

By utilizing slow movement in a relaxed manner, T'ai Chi Ch'uan is very good for your health.

In this nuclear age why should anyone practice T'ai Chi considering how life has changed since ancient China?

Today, everyone is too aggressive. No one wishes to yield. Everybody wishes to take advantage of others. This is common in all societies and all countries. If things continue the way they are going, there will be a third world war. This has been predicted as being inevitable. If this war occurs, it will be far worse than the last because of the development of nuclear warfare. The bombs of today will not be like the two dropped on Japan in World War II. They had relatively little destructive ability. This time war will possibly demolish the world and many human beings will perish.

If everyone learned to relax, yield and lose, this predicted third world war would be avoided. If everyone learned not to be aggressive by following the principles of T'ai Chi Ch'uan, wars could be abolished. This is why I strongly

The essence of T'ai Chi is to relax, sink all of the weight downward and sink the ch'i into the tan-tien.

advocate the practice of T'ai Chi.

You say that when you practice alone it is important to imagine an opponent in front of you. Can you give an example of this?

Yes. For example, when practicing the posture, "Step Forward, Deflect Downward, Intercept and Punch", it should be followed by the "Withdraw and Push" posture. With these two postures you *presume* that an opponent strikes to your chest with his right fist. You neutralize this by placing your right wrist, palm up, on his right wrist. Then place your left palm, facing downward, on the inside of his right forearm and press it downward. This is called "deflect". Next, step forward with your left foot and at the same time move your left arm to the front and left side. This is called "intercept." Proceed to strike his chest, using your right fist, with the "tiger mouth" facing upward. This is called "punch." These are the three movements.

The second posture is called "Withdraw and Push." The opponent seizes your right wrist as you strike out at his chest and he pushes it to the left. He does this with his left hand. You restore your body, crossing both hands together, with the palms facing the body. This is called "withdraw." Secondly, separate your palms and turn them outward. With your right hand lightly touching his right wrist, push forward with both hands using the whole body as one unit. This is called "push."

If you have nothing in your mind in which to base your practice, your forms will gradually and unconsciously change.

This is the only way to practice T'ai Chi Ch'uan. If you have nothing in your mind in which to base your practice, your forms will gradually and unconsciously change. The functional uses of T'ai Chi will eventually be lost. Professor Cheng Man-ch'ing told us this often. He said, "When practicing T'ai Chi alone, you must imagine that there is an opponent in front of you. This is one of the secret techniques I learned from the Yang family." It is very important that you do this.

What is mind-intent?

When you practice T'ai Chi Ch'uan, on a solo basis, it should be done with what is called "imagination." This means that when you wish to push someone over, you do it with your mind. You do not actually use muscular force; you only use your mind. Through being completely relaxed, your mind will gradually presume that there is an opponent in front of you. You will push him over, even though there is no one there.

Let us suppose that I wish to push you over through use of my mind only. Even though I do not use energy I will push you for a great distance because the ch'i will follow immediately the mind's command. This stage can be reached only by consistent, daily practice without using the slightest bit of energy.

At this level, when you practice pushing-hands with someone, your mind will immediately take over; the ch'i will come out and you will knock him over instantly. This is imagination becoming reality.

Can you tell us exactly what you mean by the Three Treasures: ching, ch'i and shen?

The Chinese call the three treasures *san pao. Ching* is the sperm, the sexual secretions of both the male and female. *Ch'i* (life giving principle) is a kind of oxygen in the blood necessary for stamina and vitality. *Shen* is the spirit of vitality.

These three energies are within your person. They transfer from one to another. The ching will transfer to ch'i and the ch'i to shen. They rotate inside the body making you stronger and stronger. If the ching is weak or lost, that person will be sick. By practicing T'ai Chi Ch'uan, you will mobilize your energy so that the ching can be transferred into ch'i and from the ch'i into shen.

When a person is young and strong, the sperm is abundant. In an old man it is exhausted. Even if the sperm is abundant, though, trouble may come if you do not transfer it into ch'i. This "ching" or sexual secretion is not the same as the similar term used for intrinsic energy. Both words transliterate the same but are entirely different in meaning. When the ch'i is full, it likewise must be transferred into shen, the spirit of vitality. All three energies must transfer from one to another if one is to enjoy good health.

The spirit of vitality is expressed in your eyes. If it is strong, it is possible to see for a great distance. If it is weak, you can see only a few feet away. Eventually, that person will see nothing at all. When the three treasures are strong, you will be in perfect health.

What do you mean by "transferring?"

To *transfer* means to change. The Taoists say, "*lien ching wai ch'i*"which means to "cultivate the sperm and transfer it into ch'i." Ching is the sperm and it is necessary to stimulate it. The best method to accomplish this is by practicing T'ai Chi Ch'uan. Gradually the ching will transfer into ch'i and the ch'i will penetrate the bones and become marrow. All three energies will return to their normal level as they are closely connected to one another. Animals are able to do this naturally. A tiger, for example, is very strong because the ch'i has penetrated the bone naturally and has turned into marrow. When the bones are filled with marrow, they are very strong.

In the T'ai Chi classics it says, "suspend the head from above as if being held up by a string" or "retain a light and sensitive energy on top of the head." These are both ways in which to stimulate the spirit of vitality. It also says in the classics, "When the lowest vertebrae are plumb erect, the spirit of vitality reaches the top of head. With the top of the head suspended from above, as if by a thread, the whole body will feel light and nimble." This means that the practice of T'ai Chi Ch'uan is very good for a person's health because the spirit of vitality will become very strong.

It seems that there is a strong relationship between ch'i and intrinsic energy. Would you explain this?

To strike with the ch'i is to use intrinsic energy. It is important to exhale during the strike as this will allow the ch'i inside to come out. Without intrinsic energy the ch'i will just sit inside because it cannot get out by itself.

Suppose that during the strike, you inhale instead of exhale. This will be injurious because the ch'i will remain inside. If, however, you exhale when striking, the strike will be much more effective. Ch'i, when combined with the ching

Your mind will immediately take over; the ch'i will come out and you will knock him over instantly. This is imagination becoming reality.

is very powerful.

When you strike someone, the opponent will feel the intrinsic energy only and not the ch'i. The person performing the strike will feel only his ch'i and not the intrinsic energy. They are closely connected.

So breathing is important here too?

Yes. I will give a few examples of breathing properly and explain how effective it is, if done correctly. The first one, I mentioned already, about exhaling when striking someone. But, suppose that your opponent is stronger than you and his energy comes back at you. Let's say he even pushes you over. Even though you fall, you will not be hurt unless you were inhaling as it happened. If you hold your breath when striking, you will be like a piece of wood, strong but not pliable. When you fall it is like one hard thing hitting another and you will be hurt. If you exhale, your body will be relaxed and flexible and little injury will occur. Children are like this. They are very soft and relaxed and when a child falls, it is rarely hurt. This is important when you are being pushed over. Do not tense up or the result will be worse.

When confronted by a man who is superior in skill, try to relax. It is difficult but necessary because if you tense up, you will do poorly. The psychological aspect of a confrontation is significant. You must keep your body under control.

In your book you discuss former heaven ch'i and early heaven ch'i. What do you mean by these two terms and how do they relate to T'ai Chi Ch'uan practice?

These terms mean the ch'i before heaven and after heaven. Although they are different, the result of each is the same. When practicing some will do it the way of "hsien tien hsi" and others by the method of "hou tien hsi". These terms mean reverse breathing and natural breathing, respectively.

Natural breathing, hou tien hsi, is the method in which the stomach becomes larger when the person inhales. When exhaling, it contracts and becomes smaller.

A great number of people that practice T'ai Chi Ch'uan use hsien tien hsi or reverse breathing. With reverse breathing, the stomach contracts as the person breathes in. Breathing out, it expands. With this type of breathing, one can acquire the art faster than by using the natural method but the final result is the same. Both methods are good. Which one you use is up to you. I prefer the hou tien hsi because it is the more natural way.

Some schools of T'ai Chi talk about the upper and lower tan-tien, referring to the "third eye" and navel areas, calling it upper and lower level ch'i. What relationship do these have with before heaven ch'i and after heaven ch'i?

These things have nothing to do with the T'ai Chi way of breathing. When you exhale, the ch'i comes from the tan-tien which is one and one-third inches below the navel. The ch'i is stored here and it is from this area that it flows throughout the body. It does not come from the head. This is not the T'ai Chi way of practice.

I prefer the hou tien hsi because it is the more natural way.

When we practice T'ai Chi, how should we breathe and what is the role of breathing in T'ai Chi Ch'uan?

First let's discuss what a beginner must remember when practicing. A beginner must know the name of the posture, what direction to face, the number of beats and many other things. This will be done breathing naturally and without music. Eventually the beginner will do everything to the music. If, however, the person forgets the music, the breath will be used as a guide, that is, breathing will be used to control the beats. On the first beat, there is an inhalation, on the second beat, an exhalation, on the third, an inhalation and on the fourth, an exhalation. An exhalation should always occur on the last beat of the posture. If this is done properly, over time it will be mastered both physically and mentally.

When a person can perform the postures with or without music with nothing in their mind, they have reached the highest level. The exercise may take twenty minutes or more. The method you have learned is forgotten and even the breathing. It is done naturally, without thought, with the mind absolutely empty. The person will feel as if in a trance and when finished they will wonder what it was they did and where they were. This stage where the mind is totally empty is very good for health.

This stage where the mind is totally empty is very good for health.

When you talk about breathing, are you saying that the breath should be even in regards to the inhalation and the exhalation? Should not the exhalation be longer than the inhalation?

Yes. I have had many teachers and most of them advocated that when breathing, the exhalation be longer than the inhalation. Therefore, the inhalation is a bit quicker. It is the method I prefer.

What is the meaning of using the whole body as one unit? Is this related to intrinsic energy?

The T'ai Chi Classic by Chang San-feng says, "The entire body must be used as one unit." Therefore when you turn leftward, the body, waist and head must turn simultaneously. The head must remain in the same position as before the turn . When moving backwards or forwards, left or right, the body should move as one unit. In this way intrinsic energy will be developed. Intrinsic energy comes from the sinews and tendons. It originates from the feet, flows into the legs, then waist and is issued by the spine. The whole body must relax and push forward as one unit for intrinsic energy to be released.

To develop this you must learn not to use muscular energy when you strike out. This force is from the bone and means that the hands are working independently of the rest of the body. The ch'i will rise up and the body will become tense. After a few strikes you will become tired.

If, however, you strike with intrinsic energy, the ch'i will sink into the tantien; it will go downward not upward. Striking in this manner is like using a whip. It is tremendously powerful.

Would you please explain the ideas of hearing energy, sticking energy, neutralizing energy and attacking energy?

Hearing energy involves feeling the opponent's energy. When someone touches you, you do not hear a sound but immediately you know him. This means that you are aware of his intent and actions. You will feel his slightest stir and, therefore, will be able to act. The development of this form of energy will mean being able to determine the real from the unreal, that is, whether the opponent is faking or not. It will enable you to know in what direction to neutralize by just how the opponent touches your body. You will know whether he is strong or weak.

Sticking energy means the opponent cannot get rid of you. It is as if you were plaster attached to his body. If you move, he must follow. If you go forward, he must retreat and if you retreat, he must come forward. With this type of energy, the opponent is under your complete control.

Neutralizing energy involves getting rid of your opponent's energy when it comes to you. Doing this disallows his energy from coming in contact with your body. This is accomplished by learning how to yield and lose.

Attacking energy means to use a counter-offensive technique on your opponent. You must use intrinsic energy which involves using the whole body as one unit. This is not easy because, first, it is necessary to master all of the techniques.

When you speak of attacking energy, you say that there are many different types of attacking energy, such as prolonged energy, abrupt energy, lowering energy and sinking energy. What do all of these mean?

These energies all depend on the action of your opponent. To *prolong*, means to take your opponent a long, long way. Sometimes it is necessary to use just a jerking movement which is very abrupt, letting go immediately afterwards. Depending upon your opponent, you may have to go further by either *lowering, raising, sinking* or *pulling*. If you encounter resistance you must use a technique; if there is no resistance, you can just push him over.

Why are these terms defined as energies? Why are they not called "forces" or something of that nature?

When you relax, you do not use force. Force comes from the bone and energy comes from the sinews and tendons. To generate energy one must not only be sensitive, relaxed and alert but use the whole body as one unit. Force involves tension and the use of external musculature. Energy is internal and is issued mostly from the spine.

Force is used in the external martial styles, like karate and kung-fu, because individual limbs are employed with limited use of the whole body. Internal systems, such as T'ai Chi Ch'uan, develop various energies through relaxation and the use of the entire body as one unit.

What is sticky energy?

Sticky energy is divided into three levels: lowest, middle and highest. The lowest level requires that you touch the opponent's body with the hand in order to push him over. There are two methods for this. One is borrowing his energy in order to issue your own energy. This is called the "receive-attack" technique. The other is to entice your opponent to issue his energy and, then, after neutral-

> *Sticking energy means the opponent cannot get rid of you. It is as if you were plaster attached to his body.*

izing all his energy to one side, you knock him over with the "roll-back" technique. These two techniques are the most elemental methods used in T'ai Chi pushing hands.

The middle level of sticky energy is described by the saying, "as soon as you touch the clothing of the other man, he is already in your trap." No sooner does your palm attach to his clothing than he is uprooted. At this level he can be thrown in any of eighteen ways.

A person with the highest level of sticky energy can use his flat palm to lift anything without exerting strength through the fingers. One of the Yang family disciples, Chen Hsui-feng, relied only on the sticky energy of one palm to raise a heavy armchair and carry it from one spot to another. So, it is said in the T'ai Chi classics, "with the mind-intent, the ch'i follows." His palm was full of electromagnetic-like energy to which the armchair was irresistibly attracted. This is the most developed form of sticky energy. It is an art that is almost completely lost.

Master Liang can you describe pushing-hands?

The second goal of T'ai Chi Ch'uan is self-defense. For self-defense you must learn pushing-hands. This exercise consists usually of four movements. They are ward-off, rollback, press and push.

In practice they would be used as follows:

1. You would *Push* me and I would *Roll-Back*.
2. Then, you would perform *Press* on me and I would neutralize it.
3. 1 would *Push* you and you would do *Roll-Back*.
4. 1 would *Press* and you would neutralize.

These movements are repeated, back and forth in this manner. The reason for doing this exercise is to learn to neutralize, relax, yield and lose.

In pushing-hands you must entice the opponent into advancing and then, when his energy is emptied, adhere to him and issue energy. Adhere, join, stick and follow without letting go and without resistance. This is the correct method for pushing-hands.

The most important movement of the four, according to my teacher, is the roll-back posture. When you have mastered the roll-back posture and its application, you will have mastered one half of T'ai Chi.

This is how roll-back is used. When you push me and I can't take it anymore, without losing my balance, I neutralize with the roll-back technique. I must let your energy go to the side and not to my body. If the push comes on my left arm, I neutralize with my left palm turning upwards. This is a secret technique that came from the Yang family. This movement is very important if the posture is to be effective.

What is the procedure for learning pushing-hands?

The process for learning pushing-hands involves three steps. The first step is to acquire a root or "central equilibrium." This means that it is very difficult for your opponent to push you over. What is important is that when you practice pushing-hands you do not reveal this root. This would be force against force and in direct opposition to T'ai Chi principles.

When you have mastered the roll-back posture and its application, you will have mastered one half of T'ai Chi.

The next step is to learn how to lose. As mentioned earlier, you will develop softness and suppleness in yielding to your opponent's push.

The third step is the counter-offense. This involves attacking and pushing your opponent over. It is not that easy, though. It means that you will have to discover your opponent's yin and yang areas or substantial and insubstantial aspects.

You must find his center of gravity. A successful push requires that you know this. Next, you must determine the line. Altogether, there are twenty-five lines. The line you choose will depend on the opponent's position so the push will not necessarily be straight.

Next, it is important to avoid being double-weighted. You must relax and use the whole body as one unit in your push. This will allow you to use intrinsic energy. When these conditions are met, you can push effectively.

This all means that in order to break your opponent's root, you must know your superior position and his defective one. These are things to know or be capable of doing in order to push successfully:

1. The substantial and insubstantial of the opponent's body.
2. Center of balance.
3. Lines of attack or opponent's defective position.
4. Using your whole body as one unit (intrinsic energy).

Your counterattack will be of little use if you do not pay attention to these points.

After a long period of training, as soon as your hand touches the opponent's body, you will know whether your push will be effective or not. Everything will be in your mind, already, so you will know instantly in what direction to push. If you do not know, it will be a matter of "blind man's buff", that is, you will only be guessing.

You say that when you push, there must be a circle and when you punch, the second you make contact the fist turns. Are these two actions related?

Yes, both employ *corkscrew* energy. If it is used properly it will penetrate directly into the opponent's body like a screw. You do not use just the hand in this strike, though. If you do, you will be using external muscular force which will not affect the opponent internally. You must use the intrinsic energy, that is, the whole body as one unit as I have mentioned before. Externally, nothing will be apparent but internally there will be an injury.

It is a tremendously powerful strike. Every time you push or strike, you must use this circle or corkscrew motion. Even when pushing in a straight line, it is necessary to use this motion. The hand must turn slightly but with the whole body. By doing this, you will be utilizing the intrinsic energy to the greatest degree. This is rather difficult to express unless a teacher demonstrates it.

When you push someone, you do not appear to move much at all. How is it that you can push someone over like this?

When you actually push someone it is important that you do not lean forward or actually push forward. The push should be executed with just a turning motion, a release of the breath and a sinking motion. You must use your whole

*B*oth employ corkscrew energy. If it is used properly it will penetrate directly into the opponent's body like a screw.

body as one unit, sink down and "push", without going forward.

It is important to keep your equilibrium during the push or you will put yourself into a defective position. Move as one unit, keep your back perfectly erect and the push will be performed correctly.

The power of the push originates from the foot, moves to the leg and is issued by the spine. It has nothing to do with the hands. When I push, you will see little movement and sometimes none at all. It looks invisible but I will push you far away. My teacher taught me this and did it to me many times. I would not see his hands move but I would be pushed for a great distance. Practicing pushing-hands and the forms will gradually develop this energy. This can only be accomplished, however, through constant practice.

T.T. practices push-hands with Susan Spero.

What does gaining a root mean?

A root means "central equilibrium". When you stand and someone tries to push you over but can't, this is central equilibrium. Your feet will be rooted just like a tree. It is possible to acquire this by performing the T'ai Chi Ch'uan exercises daily at least two or three times. A root is very important and little else can be achieved in T'ai Chi until a person obtains one. When no one can push you over, you can learn how to yield. From yielding you will learn how to counterattack. Everything is done step by step.

So, first, a beginner must acquire a root, through daily practice of T'ai Chi Ch'uan. Even though I'm over eighty-five years old, a young man cannot push me over because I've been practicing for so many years. I've naturally developed a root. If you don't believe me, try it.

What do you mean by learning how to lose and how is this useful for self defense?

Learning how to lose means to not use force against force. When energy comes to your body, do not resist. This is called "small loss, small gain, big loss, big gain."

When your opponent pushes, you must yield. Eventually no one will be able to put their energy on your body. Gradually your body will become soft and you will bend like a willow tree.

In the T'ai Chi classics it says, "your waist will be as though boneless." To attain this degree of pliability, you must be very soft but once it has been attained, no one will be able to touch you. This is all accomplished by learning how to lose.

The classics also say, "To yield means to attack; to withdraw means to attack." These two movements occur simultaneously. To yield, let your opponent come to you and then neutralize his energy; lead him into your trap, then

The power of the push originates from the foot, moves to the leg and is issued by the spine. It has nothing to do with the hands.

go forward and attack him. In this way, losing will enable a small person to overcome a much larger opponent. If force against force is used, the stronger man will win.

Please explain a little about the two-person dance set.

The two-person dance involves moving with a partner. It may be performed to music. Every posture in the two-person set consists of three movements done in slow motion. They are: *neutralize, seize* and *attack*. The dance will teach that when someone strikes at you, it is necessary to first neutralize the attack, then seize (attach to) the limb or opponent's body and strike back. You will be able to do this properly only after a great deal of practice. Although it is done slowly in the two-person set, after a period of time, all three movements will be performed very quickly.

When it comes to learning the practical use of T'ai Chi, the two-person dance is excellent. I will give an example of its usage. When an opponent strikes with his hands, you must know the correct way to neutralize, that is, to neutralize your body in order to avoid his strike.

For the second movement, you must put your body into a superior position. This is done by adjusting your waist and legs. Immediately hold his arm or lightly touch his body in order to understand (interpret) his center of balance and substantial and insubstantial aspects.

The third movement involves putting your opponent into a defective position. Feel his joints and then immediately strike. When striking, remember what I have said before, that the body must be relaxed and used as one unit.

The T'ai Chi classics say, "The hands and feet should be relaxed and the waist must act as one unit so that when advancing and retreating you will obtain a good opportunity and a superior position." If you fail to gain these advantages, your body will be in a state of disorder and confusion. The only way to correct this fault is by adjusting your waist and legs.

It is a dance when one posture is divided into three movements: one, *da*; two, *da*; three, *da*. When the three movements are combined into one, it is a knock-out technique.

When you have mastered the techniques of the two-person dance, you will know the functional use of the one hundred and fifty postures of T'ai Chi Ch'uan.

How important is the practice of pushing-hands to T'ai Chi Ch'uan?

If you only practice the solo forms you will gradually acquire a root or central equilibrium. This is very important but you will never be able to interpret the strength of your opponent if you do not do two-person drills like pushing-hands.

Pushing-hands practice is necessary for learning self-defense skills. You will learn how to find a person's yin and yang aspects and locate his center of gravity. Every person is different. You will learn not to be double-weighted when you confront an opponent. Also you will learn to find the opponent's line of attack so you can push him over easily.

If you do not practice pushing-hands, you will not learn these things. It is

*W*hen you have mastered the techniques of the two-person dance, you will know the functional use of the one hundred and fifty postures of T'ai Chi Ch'uan.

necessary to use your hand to interpret and solo drills will not teach you this. I believe that a person cannot acquire a high level of skill if they do not practice pushing-hands.

T.T. practices the two person dance with Susan Spero.

When speaking of the martial aspects of T'ai Chi Ch'uan, you say that the substantial and insubstantial must be clearly differentiated. What do you mean by that?

Substantial means hard or solid and insubstantial means soft or empty. It is very important to realize this when engaged in pushing-hands. A large part of pushing-hands practice involves trying to find the opponent's center of gravity. As soon as his center is found, a push will be successful because he will not be able to neutralize it. If on the other hand, his body is found to be soft and empty, he will be able to neutralize your attack. Knowing his substantial and insubstantial, that is, where he is solid and where he is empty is necessary for an effective attack.

If you find the substantial, pushing will be easy but if not, it will be necessary to make him move by pulling his hands or by using some other tactic. This will aid in finding the substantial part of his body so he can be pushed over.

To ensure an attack's success, you must know your opponent. Remember, if you cannot test or interpret your opponent's yin and yang, substantial and insubstantial, you do not know him.

A person cannot acquire a high level of skill if they do not practice pushing-hands.

Why is it necessary to practice T'ai Chi with weapons?

To practice T'ai Chi without weapons, that is to practice only the empty-hand sets, is to strengthen the muscles of the body and not the sinews and tendons. Weapon practice will strengthen the sinews and tendons. When the body, hands and weapon act as one unit, the intrinsic energy will reach to the tip of the weapon. Therefore, intrinsic energy can be developed to the fullest extent and to the highest level. Practice without weapons will mean that the intrinsic energy will reach only as far as the finger tips.

For example, this sword, here in my hand, must be used with the whole body as one unit. It should not be used with only the arm. In ancient times people trained to be soft and delicate with the sword. They did not try merely to develop strength and generate force. Daily practice will enable the intrinsic energy to come out. If it is not developed, a person will be unable to push an opponent far away when engaged in empty-hand fighting. This is why it is necessary to practice T'ai Chi with weapons, so use the sword, sabre and staff.

How would you know a true T'ai Chi master?

The arms of a true T'ai Chi master are like iron bars wrapped in cotton. They are extremely flexible but internally strong and heavy. When grasping an opponent's hand as in pushing-hands practice, the T'ai Chi master's hands are very light but the opponent cannot get away from him. He can release intrinsic energy from his spine like the bullet from the muzzle of a gun. His strike is lightning swift and clear cut like the breaking of a stick, without the slightest exertion of muscular force.

As soon as an opponent feels a slight stir of his body, he is already pushed more than ten feet away without feeling any pain. When the T'ai Chi master attaches his hands lightly to the hands of an opponent, without grasping them, they are as firm as glue. It is impossible to remove them and they will cause a terrible aching and numbness in the opponent's arms.

Trying to subdue or restrain a T'ai Chi master is like attempting to catch the wind. You end up with nothing at all. It is like stepping on a gourd in the water; it is so slippery that it is impossible to get a firm hold or footing. This is the real meaning of self-defense in T'ai Chi. These are the words of my teacher's teacher, Yang Cheng-fu. They are accurate and precise. My teacher proved them true, gaining my great respect.

Trying to subdue or restrain a T'ai Chi master is like attempting to catch the wind. You end up with nothing at all.

One last question, sir?
How many last questions?

This is it. If T. T. Liang had one wish, what would it be?
I wish that all my students will become better than me. That is my wish. I wish also that everyone would practice T'ai Chi Ch'uan because it is an exercise for all people, the sick, young and old. Attaining this will be very difficult. It is all up to you.

This interview was recorded by Stuart Olson and
Johnathan Russell in 1986.

CHAPTER TWO
ANECDOTES OF THE YANG FAMILY

Within the Chinese martial arts there are numerous categories and styles. Only the Wu-Tang school of T'ai Chi Ch'uan, handed down by the Taoist saint, Chang San-feng, is the pure internal system of these martial art varieties. Only through the method of relaxing the whole body, without exerting the slightest external muscular force, will the intrinsic energy be developed. This is the fundamental principle of the Wu-Tang school of T'ai Chi Ch'uan.

The Story of Yang Lu-chan

Yang Lu-chan, a native of Kuang Ping in Hopei province, received his T'ai Chi instruction from Chen Chang-hsing of Honan province. Yang Lu-chan handed down his art to his two sons, Pan-hou and Chien-hou, and Chien-hou to his sons, Shao-hou and Cheng-fu. The following is a general account of the anecdotes of the Yang family and their disciples. It is according to what has been recorded about this illustrious family.

Yang Lu-chan had studied the external systems of martial art such as the hard style of Shaolin Boxing. Later he learned of Chen Chang-hsing, a native of Chen Chia Kuo (Chen family village) of Hwai Ching Prefecture in Honan province. Chen Chang-hsing was well versed in T'ai Chi Ch'uan, an internal system of martial art. Yang Lu-chan took all the money he had and travelled to Honan province to learn from Chen Chang-hsing.

Although he studied for several years, he was always defeated when testing himself with his fellow students. One night he got up to urinate and heard a strange sound coming from the other side of the wall. He climbed over it to find out what was happening. He saw that all his fellow students were gathered inside the great hall and that the teacher was explaining and demonstrating all the secret principles and techniques of T'ai Chi. Yang Lu-chan then concealed himself outside the window of the hall and watched. On returning to his room he practiced diligently what he could remember. From then on, he went to watch them every night without fail.

After a period of time, when some of his fellow students forced him to contest, Yang Lu-chan had no alternative but to consent, with the result that no one could overcome him. All his fellow students were astonished. His teacher then called Yang Lu-chan and said, "I have examined you for several years and found you are an honest and sincere young man, with much patience, so I will, in person, show you the real meaning of T'ai Chi Ch'uan. Come to my room tomorrow."

The next day he went to see his teacher and found him sitting in his chair napping, bobbing his head in a very uncomfortable manner. Yang Lu-chan stood quietly by his side for a long time but his teacher did not wake up. Thereupon, he supported his teacher's head with his hands for such a long time that he felt as though his arms were breaking. He dared not move at all. When his teacher finally awakened, he said, "You are already here. I was tired and fell asleep. Come again tomorrow." Lu-chan left.

Only through the method of relaxing the whole body, without exerting the slightest external muscular force, will the intrinsic energy be developed.

The next day he went back at the appointed time and again found his teacher fast asleep. Lu-chan waited with bated breath. His teacher occasionally opened his eyes. Seeing Lu-chan standing there waiting calmly by his side, without any expression of resentment, he again said, "Come back tomorrow."

When Lu-chan arrived on the third day, his teacher said, "This young man is worth teaching. " From that day he taught Lu-chan the secrets of Chen's T'ai Chi and ordered him to practice when he returned home. Afterwards, whenever Lu-chan engaged in a contest with his fellow students, no one could overcome him. He was second to none.

One day, as Lu-chan was preparing to return to his home town, his teacher summoned everyone to meet together in the hall. Pointing to all of his own family disciples, he said, "I have taught all of you the secrets of T'ai Chi and none of you have acquired it." Next, pointing to Lu-chan, he said, "But I reluctantly gave my art to this man. Although he is not of our Chen clan, he, nonetheless, has obtained the essence of my art. He is now leaving." After Yang Lu-chan had fulfilled his ambitions to the utmost, he returned home.

Lu-chan returned home penniless. Someone recommended him to teach at a rich family's home in the capital (Beijing). The rich family had already engaged one boxing teacher, whose martial skill was mediocre at best. This teacher became very jealous when Lu-chan came to teach in the same place. The jealous man insisted on a duel with Lu-chan. Lu-chan said, "If you really want to fight, please inform the head of the family first." He did so and the host agreed, but said, "I hope you both will take it as a friendly match; that you will set limits and not cause injury or death."

Without even seeing Lu-chan lift his hands, the jealous teacher was thrown more than ten feet away.

Lu-chan arrived in the arena and stood erect without moving. The jealous teacher then suddenly extended his fist to hit Lu-chan with all his might. Without even seeing Lu-chan lift his hands, the jealous teacher was thrown more than ten feet away. The host was greatly surprised. He bowed in deep respect and said, "I did not know that the level of your art was so profound and abstruse and was of such a high degree." Thereupon, he spread a sumptuous feast to honor him. After the banquet Lu-chan packed up and resigned his post. He then settled down within the capital city and taught Yang style T'ai Chi. So the people learning T'ai Chi in the capital were all Yang's disciples.

Pan-Hou

Yang Lu-chan handed down his art of T'ai Chi to his two sons, Pan-hou and Chien-hou. He expected his sons to acquire his art as quickly as possible, admonishing them to practice day and night without rest. While Pan-hou and Chien-hou were under their father's supervision, they met with unbearable treatment in their training. Pan-hou attempted to run away from home but was intercepted and brought home. Chien-hou even once tried to hang himself but was rescued in the nick of time.

Though they had not yet reached the age of twenty, they were already well known for their talent and ability. Their reputations were held high all over the capital. A nobleman heard of them and engaged Pan-hou as an instructor, offering him forty dollars per month salary. He showed Pan-hou great respect and bestowed honors upon him.

Mr. Liu of Hsiung Hsien practiced, "Yueh's irregular postures". He was of great strength, being capable of raising more than 500 pounds and had more than one thousand students learning from him. Somebody provoked hostilities on both sides. Pan-hou, who was a proud man, was unable to endure this provocation. He challenged Mr. Liu to a duel, which was to take place in the east city. The news spread throughout the capital and several thousand spectators gathered at the arena. After much of the crowd arrived, Mr. Liu immediately stretched out his hand and grasped Pan-hou's wrist tightly. Pan-hou applied the technique of, "intercepting energy to shake off and attack" which caused Mr. Liu to fall. He immediately left in great distress. As a result of the contest, Pan-hou's reputation spread far and wide; his name was held in high esteem on both sides.

Two tigers meet. (Painting by T.T. Liang)

When he returned home to see his father, he was elated with his victory. With a look of exultation, he gave a detailed account of how he knocked down Mr. Liu. His father gave a cold-hearted laugh and said, "Your strike was good enough but half your sleeve has been torn away. Is this called T'ai Chi?" Pan-hou looked down at his sleeve and found it was indeed the truth. He was downcast and left the house. He then recalled that when Mr. Liu had seized his wrist, it was like a dog's bite. After having received such a shock he practiced T'ai Chi more diligently than ever in order to improve himself.

Your strike was good enough but half your sleeve has been torn away. Is this called T'ai Chi?

Fu Erh-yeh Reminisces

Yang Cheng-fu said that his uncle, Yang Pan-hou, had a disciple named Fu Erh-yeh who lived at Chao Mien Lane in the east city. He was over seventy years of age but his appearance was that of a man in his fifties. His son was fifty some years old and everyone thought that they were brothers. Fu Erh-yeh commented, "Though I am the disciple of Yang Pan-hou, I am unable to hand down his art for I have not practiced in more than thirty years.

My father did not allow me to practice T'ai Chi for this reason. Formerly, my elder brother learned the art of wrestling diligently without intermission. After several years he returned home. As soon as he saw me he asked, "How is your wrestling technique?" I told him I had not practiced it for a long time. I told him that I had learned T'ai Chi Ch'uan from Yang Pan-hou, who taught me how to relax and use the internal intrinsic energy and not the external muscular force. I said he also taught me how to neutralize an opponent's strength.

My brother ridiculed me and would not believe in it whatsoever, so he struck out his fist to hit me. I used the T'ai Chi posture "Deflect Downward, Intercept and Punch" to counterattack. Unexpectedly my brother fell away through the hall to the outside yard. He lay on the ground face up and he could not get up, having been injured by the fall. He rested for several days and began to recover. I was severely reprimanded by my father and not allowed to practice T'ai Chi from then on. How pitiable it was, simply because I was too young and reckless."

Fu Erh-yeh continued his story. "My teacher's father, Yang Lu-chan, was fond of me, owing to my diligence and carefulness. I often stood at his side to serve him and fill his pipe with tobacco. At age eighty, Yang Lu-chan still vigorously practiced T'ai Chi Ch'uan daily without intermission. Occasionally he came to my house to chat. On one of these visits it was raining and the road was full of mud. When he arrived, I noticed that the soles of his shoes were white and clean as if they never touched the mud. They were without a speck of dirt. This is called, "the technique of treading on the snow without trace of a footstep." This is possible because the body of a T'ai Chi master is so light and nimble that he can raise his body up. When this is practiced to the highest level, he can raise his body up and walk in the air. Pan-hou had already acquired this technique but very few knew of it.

When this is practiced to the highest level, he can raise his body up and walk in the air.

The Death of Yang Lu-chan

Yang Lu-chan summoned his senior disciples by letter, asking them all to come to his house on a certain day. He intended to travel and he had some words of instruction for them. They all arrived at the appointed time but they thought something was strange because there was no cart ready outside the gate. When they went inside, they saw their teacher (Lu-chan) seated in the middle of the great hall. After all the disciples saluted him, each one helped fill his pipe with tobacco and then stood quietly by his side. Lu-chan called them one by one and spoke words of encouragement to them. He talked to them about the general principles of T'ai Chi. After a little while, Lu-chan suddenly brushed his sleeves, sat erect and passed away. After his death, his coffin was put in a monastery outside Chi Hua gate.

The monastery's five main halls faced south. On the east and west sides there were several sub-rooms. The coffin rested in the west sub-hall. Yang Pan-hou and his brother, Chien-hou, all lived in the west sub-hall. I also lived there so that I could serve them.

Later a southerner arrived at the monastery. He had very long fingernails and his speech was slurred. No one knew who he was, nor could they understand his words. One day my teacher came out from his room and said to me, "Don't go out from this gate and do not talk with the southerner in the east sub-hall." I promised I would not but wondered the reason why. At that time I was only nineteen and quite immature. When my teacher, Yang Pan-hou, left I stayed behind. I sat there quietly and after a period of time I needed to move about. I forgot the promise I had previously made to my teacher. I opened the gate and went into the main hall to play. In my right hand I held a cup full of tea and was spinning it around as I danced about. I jumped up onto a small table without spilling a drop. Just then I was seen by the southerner. He asked me questions about myself but I did not answer, as I remembered my teacher's order. I was frightened and returned to my own room.

The next day the chief monk of the monastery, who also knew the secret techniques of the martial arts quite well, had an earnest talk with Pan-hou. At first my teacher was troubled. I could see his face turn color. After a while he nodded his head and agreed to something. The monk went out and a little while later returned to my teacher, accompanied by the southerner. Pan-hou treated the southerner with unusual politeness. The three went out through the gate together. Later my teacher returned with a pleased look on his face. The southerner then packed up and left. No one ever said for sure, but considering all the mystery surrounding this southerner, I surmised that he was some form of a spirit body of Yang Lu-chan. This of course is just my opinion.

A Surprising Levitation

Yang Pan-hou had a daughter aged seventeen. She was a very beautiful and clever young lady whom my teacher loved very much. She died suddenly while he was away from home. When he heard the tragic news he immediately rushed home The coffin, however, had already been closed. His pain and grief was so extreme over the loss of his beautiful daughter that his body suddenly raised off the floor seven to eight feet high, as if suspended in the air. The bystanders looked at him in awe.

I had seen him do this on a few other occasions. He was capable of this as he had knowledge of the secret technique of levitation. His father, Yang Lu-chang taught him this art. Pan-hou's pain was so extreme that without even realizing it, he disclosed his extraordinary technique and skill."

Pan-hou's Sticky Energy

Although the Yang brothers, Chien-hou and Pan-hou, were well versed in the martial art of T'ai Chi Ch'uan and were very well known, they usually kept their art secret and would not show it off. They especially knew how to control their tempers and had not the slightest intention of flaunting their supremacy. They were extraordinarily humble and modest. People not well acquainted with them often mistook them for fools. It is true, indeed, that great wisdom seems like folly and great valor appears as cowardice. So a man should not be judged solely by his appearance or mannerisms.

One year a southerner (Cantonese) came to visit with Yang Pan-hou who was then already over sixty years old. The southerner showed him great respect and in admiration said, "I have heard that the sticking energy of T'ai Chi Ch'uan is excellent. It is like glue on the body and one is unable to get rid of it. I would sincerely like some instruction from you." Pan-hou replied, "I have learned from my ancestor (Yang Lu-chan) and know only a little of this art. I really do not possess such talent as you describe." So the southerner's request was obstinately refused.

But the southerner requested instruction over and over again. Pan-hou then

His pain and grief was so extreme over the loss of his beautiful daughter that his body suddenly raised off the floor seven to eight feet high, as if suspended in the air.

said, "I am sure that you are well versed in this art, but as old and worthless as I am, how can I compete with you?" After a momentary pause, Pan-hou said, "Please show me the method of test and let us see whether or not I can exert my strength in pursuit of the goal." The southerner happily responded, "Let us try this. Take several tens of bricks that have been evenly placed in the yard with a distance of two feet between each one, like a T'ai Chi round form. We will both stand on the bricks. I will be in front and you will follow in back with your hand lightly touching my back. We start to walk round and round, like turning a mill, without letting our feet touch the ground. You must not let go of my back. If your feet touch the ground or if your hand gets away from my back, it will be considered a defeat."

Pan-hou replied, "Mill Turning Round Walking" will easily make you giddy and I am afraid I won't be able to make it. But as long as you have raised the question, I cannot but obey your order and put forth my best effort to try my luck at this." So in the yard they started to arrange the bricks as the southerner had suggested. As soon as everything was in order, the southerner stepped onto the bricks, walking slowly in front. Pan-hou, sinking the ch'i to his tan-tien and concentrating his spirit of vitality within, followed behind with his hand lightly attached to the southerner's back for several rounds.

The body of the southerner was light as a swallow and his steps grew faster and faster like a flying wheel. Pan-hou applied his "Flying Upward To Chase The Wind And To Pursue The Lightning" technique to follow him, so that he would not separate from him. The southerner found that there was no way in which to get rid of Pan-hou, so he suddenly raised his body and flew up onto the roof of the house. He then turned his head, looked down into the courtyard and found no trace of Pan-hou. He was very frightened. But as he turned his head back again, he found Pan-hou was still behind him with his hand lightly touching his back as before. Pan-hou then said, "You really made fun of me. I am tired now, why don't we get down and rest a little while?"

The southerner was greatly startled and could not but highly respect Pan-hou. They had made a warm friendship. The southerner later went on his way.

The Profound Skills of T'ai Chi Ch'uan

Yang Chien-hou was an instructor of the Shen Wu Battalion at the age of seventy. Chien-hou could hold a swallow in his palm without letting the bird fly away. A bird about to take off must first press downwards with its feet and find a firm foothold upon which to exert energy so as to raise its body aloft. Chien-hou could interpret the sinking energy of the bird's two claws. As the bird would push downwards, he would relax and neutralize; the swallow, unable to avail itself of a foothold, could not fly away. From this we can see the clever, subtle and ingenious use of interpreting and neutralizing energy that Chien-hou had acquired. No one else could approach his level of ability.

One day, on his way home, a coarse fellow took him by surprise and attacked him with a club from the rear. Chien-hou, with a sudden turn of his body, held the club with his hand and with a slight push, sent the man flying more than twenty feet.

Chien-hou could hold a swallow in his palm without letting the bird fly away.

Yang Lu-chan had a disciple named Wang Lan-ting whose art of T'ai Chi was very profound. Unfortunately he died at a young age. It was heard that Wang Lan-ting had a disciple named Li Pin-fu who was also very skilled. Many people came to challenge him but no one could defeat him. Once a young person, who spoke with a southern accent, came to visit Li Pin-fu. The young person's hand was several inches away from a chair in the hall. Upon stretching out his hand, the chair immediately was raised up and suspended in the air. The young person wished to compete with Li Pin-fu but he modestly declined. The young man insisted. It just so happened that Li Pin-fu was holding a puppy under his left arm. He could only parry with his right arm but after several turns of his body, Li Pin-fu caused the young person to fall. Weeping bitterly, the young man left defeated. He had great skill but could not fight well.

Upon stretching out his hand, the chair immediately was raised up and suspended in the air.

CHAPTER THREE

THREE CLASSICS OF T'AI CHI CH'UAN

THE T'AI CHI CH'UAN TREATISE
T'ai Chi Ch'uan Lun
Attributed to Ancestor Chang San-feng

With every movement string all the parts together,
keeping the entire body light and nimble.
Calmly stimulate the ch'i, with the spirit of vitality
concentrated internally.
Avoid deficiency and excess; avoid projections and hollows; avoid
severance and splice.
The energy is rooted in the feet, issued through the legs, directed by
the waist, and appears in the hands and fingers.
The feet, legs and waist must act as one unit so that whether
advancing or withdrawing you will be able to obtain a superior
position and create a good opportunity.
Failure to obtain a superior position and create a good opportunity
results from the body being in a state of disorder and confusion.
To correct this adjust the waist and legs.
Likewise, upwards and downwards, forwards and backwards,
leftwards and rightwards - all these are to be directed by the
mind-intent, and not to be expressed externally.
If there is above, there must be below; if there is advance, there
must be withdraw; if there is left, there must be right.
If the initial intent is upwards, you must first have a
downward intent.
If you want to lift something upwards, you must first have the
intent of pushing downwards.
Then the root will be severed; it will be immediately and
certainly toppled.
Clearly discriminate the substantial and insubstantial.
There is an aspect of substantial and insubstantial in each part.
Considered in their entirety all things have this nature.
Chang Ch'uan (Long Boxing) is just like a long river or great
ocean rolling on without interruption.
The Thirteen Postures of Ward-Off, Roll-Back, Press, Push, Pull,
Split, Elbow-Stroke and Shoulder-Stroke are known as the
Eight Diagrams (*Pa Kua*).
Advance-Step, Withdraw-Step, Look-Left, Gaze-Right and Central
Equilibrium are known as the Five Elements (*Wu-Hsing*).
Ward-Off, Roll-Back, Press and Push are then, *Ch'ien, K'un, K'an*
and *Li*, the Four Cardinal directions.
Pull, Split, Elbow-Stroke and Shoulder-Stroke are then, *Sun, Chen,
Tui* and *Ken*, the Four Diagonal directions.

*C*learly
*discriminate
the substantial
and
insubstantial.*

Advance, Withdraw, Look-Left, Gaze-Right and Central
Equilibrium are then, Metal, Wood, Water, Fire and Earth.
Joined together they become the Thirteen Postures.

(Appended Verse):
This treatise has been handed down by Ancestor Chang San-feng of
Wu-Tang Mountain so that heroes and worthy men everywhere can
lengthen their lifes and attain longevity, not merely as a means to
martial skill.

A Brief Commentary

*Y*ou must learn things in proper sequence and allow progress to come in a gradual and natural manner, otherwise, studying for an entire lifetime will be to no avail.

The theories behind T'ai Chi Ch'uan expressed in these classic texts are not easy to comprehend because of their depth and subtlety. The techniques, moreover, are quite difficult to acquire. The correct method is of the utmost importance. You must learn things in proper sequence and allow progress to come in a gradual and natural manner, otherwise, studying for an entire lifetime will be to no avail. In the *Song of Thirteen Postures* it says, "Pay special attention to your every posture and seek out its hidden meaning, then you can acquire this art without exerting excessive effort." ✳

There are three important T'ai Chi "Classics." The first one, called *The T'ai Chi Ch'uan Treatise*, was handed down by Chang San-feng, a Taoist of the late Sung dynasty. This classic begins by saying, "With every movement string all the parts together, keeping the entire body light and nimble." The opposite of light and nimble is heavy and clumsy and the opposite of stringing all the parts together is dispersed and confused. This indicates the coordination of substantial and insubstantial and discloses the objective of the fundamental principle of T'ai Chi.

It goes on to say, "Calmly stimulate the ch'i, with the spirit of vitality concentrated internally." This again emphasizes the importance of the internal cultivation of ch'i and spirit of vitality.

The classic continues, "Avoid deficiency and excess; avoid projections and hollows; avoid severance and splice." These defects result from using external muscular force. If, however, the mind-intent is employed to direct the movements of the body, the entire body will be relaxed and pliable so as to fulfill the requirement of being "light and nimble" and of "stringing all the parts together."

Again it says, "the energy is rooted in the feet, issued through the legs, directed by the waist and appears in the hands and fingers. The feet, legs and waist must act as one unit so that whether advancing or retreating, you will be able to create a good opportunity and obtain a superior position." The above explains the systematic method of practice.

These three paragraphs, all discussing the classic handed down by Chang San-feng, have revealed the important points of the principles, methods and functions. The principles indicate the reason why, the methods indicate what ought to be and the functions reveal the efficacy of both the principles and methods. These three are all interdependent and mutually supportive of each other in practice. Not one of them should be lacking. By practicing in this way, you will accord with what is called, "the unification of civil and martial aspects; the equal importance of principle and technique and the combined cultivation of external and internal."

T'ai Chi Ch'uan is a combination of civil and martial aspects. The civil aspect stresses principles and the martial stresses techniques. Both must be taken into account; neglecting either one is not real T'ai Chi.

The civil aspect is called Tao (principles) and the martial aspect is called skill (techniques). Tao emphasizes internal cultivation; skill emphasizes external development. Cultivating one's nature (temperament) is called internal development and training the muscles and bones is called external development. Both are important and neither can be lacking. So we can see that the very best method for beginners to learn T'ai Chi Ch'uan is to unify the civil and martial aspects. Place equal importance on Tao and skill. Combine internal cultivation with external training.

When you practice T'ai Chi, it is important to direct all the movements with mind-intent. As the *Song of the True Interpretation of T'ai Chi* says, "formless and imageless (forgetting yourself), the whole body completely relaxed (internal and external united into one) and forgetful of everything, you return to the natural way (following the desire of the mind) . . . " This indicates that mind-intent has reached the ultimate stage.

The T'ai Chi Ch'uan Treatise states, "Likewise, upwards and downwards, forward and backwards, leftwards and rightwards - all these are to be directed by the mind-intent, and not to be expressed externally." Mind-intent refers to the internal spiritual function and the outer aspect refers to the movements of the postures motivated by external muscular force.

If every movement can be directed by the mind-intent within and manifested without, the internal spiritual aspect and external physical aspect will be united. The upper and lower parts of the body will move in unison. The body will instantly follow the dictates of the mind and the ch'i. Intrinsic energy will immediately reach the intended point.

It is evident that, at the beginning, if you try to use mind-intent to direct the movements, your skill will be improved by leaps and bounds. Gradually when you have mastered the use of your mind, you will be able to acquire all the techniques. Therefore, the most important guiding point of T'ai Chi Ch'uan is the use of mind-intent to direct the movements. If you can take hold of this important point and constantly comprehend the principles, you will obtain the very essence of T'ai Chi. As the T'ai Chi classics say, "The more you practice, the more skill you will obtain, and through silent remembering and through examination, you will gradually arrive at the state of being able to follow your own mind."

The most important guiding point of T'ai Chi Ch'uan is the use of mind-intent to direct the movements.

T'AI CHI CH'UAN CLASSIC
T'ai Chi Ch'uan Ching
Attributed to Immortal Wang Chung-yueh

T'ai Chi is born of Wu Chi, the mother of yin and yang.

In motion they separate; in tranquility they unite.

Without excess and without insufficiency, be bent when following, contract when reaching out.

If the opponent is hard, I am soft; this is called "receiving".

If I go with the opponent and cause him to be defective, this is called "adhering".

Respond quickly to quick movements, respond slowly to slow movements.

Even though the changes are of all kinds, the principle remains one in the same.

Through self-mastery you will gradually apprehend "interpreting energy".

From "interpreting energy" you will reach a state of shen ming (spiritual illumination).

But without a long period of arduous practice, you will be unable to suddenly possess a clear understanding.

Retain a light and sensitive energy on top of the head.

Retain a light and sensitive energy on top of the head; sink the ch'i into the tan-tien.

Do not incline and do not lean.

To suddenly disappear and suddenly appear (means):

If the left is weighted, the right becomes empty.

If the right is weighted, the left becomes empty.

Looking upwards, it seems to become higher and higher;

looking downwards, it seems to become deeper and deeper.

When advancing, it seems to become ever farther away;

when withdrawing, it seems to become closer.

A feather cannot be added, nor can a fly alight.

The opponent does not know me, but I alone know him.

This is to face a matchless hero.

At this point you attain the highest skill.

There are numerous other styles of boxing.

Although there are differences in the postures,

these other styles do not go beyond strength overcoming weakness and speed conquering slowness;

those with strength attacking those without strength;

the quick handed conquering the slow handed.

These are all just the natural abilities of Hsien T'ien (Before Heaven), and do not relate to the strengths acquired through practice and study.

In examining the statement of "four ounces removing one thousand catties", it is evident that this is not a matter of superior strength.

If you see a very old man withstanding many opponents, what has this to do with swiftness?

Stand like a balanced scale, move like a cartwheel.

Sinking the weight to one side results in adapting to circumstances.

Double-weightedness results in being impeded.

Often we see those who after many years of painstaking effort cannot employ a neutralization and are generally subdued by the opponent.

This is because they have not yet understood the fault of double-weighting.

In wanting to avoid this fault you must know yin and yang.

To adhere is to receive; to receive is to adhere.

Yin is not separate from yang; yang is not separate from yin.

The mutual coordination of yin and yang is comparable to "interpreting energy".

After you acquire "interpreting energy", the more you practice, the more skill you will obtain, and through silent remembering and thorough examination, you will gradually arrive at the state of being able to follow your own mind.

The fundamental here is to forget the self and follow others.

Most make the error of rejecting the near for what is distant.

This is called, "the slightest divergence leads you far astray".

Students must thoroughly distinguish between these aspects.

Every word of this treatise is important.

There is not one extra word or reference.

Without natural intelligence you cannot apprehend these words.

The early masters were unwilling to propagate false teachings and did not trust just anyone. They were apprehensive about transmitting their kung-fu skills to others without good reason.

To adhere is to receive; to receive is to adhere.

The second important treatise was written by Wang Chung-yueh of the Ming dynasty. In the beginning it says, "T'ai Chi (Supreme Ultimate) is born of Wu Chi (infinity) the mother of yin and yang. In motion they separate; in tranquility, they unite. Without excess and without insufficiency, be bent when following, contract when reaching out."

The above indicates that T'ai Chi was derived from the principles of the I Ching. The treatise then says, "If I go with the opponent and cause him to be defective, this is called 'adhering'. Respond quickly to quick movements, respond slowly to slow movements. Even though the changes are of all kinds, the principle remains the same." The above includes all the principles and techniques of T'ai Chi.

THE MENTAL ELUCIDATION
OF THE THIRTEEN KINETIC POSTURES
Shih San Shih Hsing Kung Hsin
Attributed to Immortal Wang Chung-yueh

The mind moves the ch'i.

Direct the ch'i so that it sinks deeply, then it can be accumulated and enter the bone.

Circulate the ch'i throughout the body, and direct it without obstruction, so that it can easily follow the mind.

To begin you must be able to raise the spirit of vitality, to avoid the defects of dullness and clumsiness.

This is called, "suspending the head upwards".

To become nimble the mind-intent and ch'i must interchangeably respond to each other, then you will achieve the most subtle pliability.

This is called, "the fluctuating changes of substantial and insubstantial".

*T*he mind moves the ch'i.

When issuing, the energy must be totally relaxed and sunk deeply, and focussed totally in one direction.

When standing, the body must be centered, upright and comfortable, and able to sustain an attack from any of the eight directions.

Direct the ch'i, as if threading the nine crooks of a pearl, penetrating between every minute crevice.

When mobilized the energy is like steel refined one hundred times over; there is no strength which cannot be overcome.

The appearance is just like that of a hawk seizing a rabbit; the shen (spirit) resembles a cat seizing a rat.

Be still like a mountain peak; move like a river current.

Storing the energy is like drawing a bow; issuing the energy is like shooting an arrow.

Seek the straight from the curved; store and then issue.

The energy is issued from the spine.

The stepping must follow the changes of the body.

To gather is to release; to release is to gather.

Severe and then rejoin.

Moving "to and fro" there must be "fold-up" (technique);
when advancing or withdrawing there must be turning and changing (techniques).

Through ultimate softness and yielding, you will later acquire ultimate hardness and strength.

Through correct breathing, you will later become supremely alert and active.

Nourish the ch'i in order to be without disease; only through bending and reserving will there be a surplus of intrinsic energy (chin).

The mind is the commander; the ch'i is the flag; the waist is the banner.

First seek to be open and expansive; after seek to be close and compact.

Then you can reach the heights of subtlety and refinement.

It is also said:

If the opponent does not move, you do not move.

At the slightest movement of the opponent, you begin moving.

Appearing relaxed, but not relaxed; prepare to expand, but not yet expanded.

The intrinsic energy (chin) may be severed, but the mind-intent is not severed.

It is also said:

First in the mind, then in the body.

Constantly relax the abdomen; seek to penetrate the ch'i into the bone.

Quiet the spirit and still the body.

Closely preserve these in the mind.

Always remember that once you move, everything moves; that once you are tranquil, everything is tranquil.

In moving "to and fro" stay connected and adhere the ch'i to the spine, allowing it to penetrate into the spine and bones.

THIRTEEN POSTURE DIAGRAM

Wu Chi

(1) WARD-OFF *Chien*

(2) ELBOW-STROKE *Tui*

(8) PULL *Sun*

(3) PUSH *Li*

(7) PRESS *Kan*

(4) SPLIT *Chen*

(6) SHOULDER-STROKE *Ken*

(5) ROLL-BACK *Kun*

GAZE-RIGHT Fire 火

LOOK-LEFT Water 水

CENTRAL EQUILIBRIUM Earth 土

RETREAT Wood 木

ADVANCE Metal 金

Stepping, be just like a cat walking; mobilize the intrinsic energy, just like reeling silk.

Internally strengthen the spirit of vitality; externally appear peaceful and at ease.

Stepping, be just like a cat walking; mobilize the intrinsic energy, just like reeling silk.

Your mind-intent must focus on the spirit of vitality, not on the ch'i (breath).

If your mind-intent is focused on the ch'i the result will be stagnation; you will have ch'i, but no strength.

The ch'i is like a cartwheel; the waist, like an axletree.

The third treatise is Wang Chung-yueh's, *Mental Elucidation of the Thirteen Kinetic Postures.* It emphasizes utmost sensitivity and accuracy as the prerequisites of practice. In the beginning this treatise states, "The mind moves the ch'i . . . " *Mind* here refers to mind-intent, which is a human perception. This is the leading principle of the entire treatise. It goes on to say, "The mind is the commander; the ch'i is the flag; the waist is the banner." Also, "First in the mind, then in the body... your mind-intent must focus on the spirit of vitality, not on the ch'i (breath)." These phrases all indicate the importance of mind-intent when practicing T'ai Chi.

The above three treatises include all the essential aspects of T'ai Chi Ch'uan, omitting none. Students must make a thorough investigation of them and comprehend their meaning deeply in order to acquire this art.

CHAPTER FOUR
THE PROCESS OF ATTAINING T'AI CHI CH'UAN

The general outline of the T'ai Chi Ch'uan exercise is divided into three levels: Man, Earth and Heaven.

The lowest level, Man, is an exercise to relax (sung) the sinews and circulate the blood. It is subdivided into three steps. The first step is to relax the sinews from the shoulders to the fingers, the second step is to relax the sinews from the thighs to the bubbling-well (yung chuan) points and the third step is to relax the sinews from the lowest vertebrae to the pai hui (crown).

The middle level, Earth, is an exercise to open and penetrate into the articulations of the joints. It is subdivided into three steps. The first step is to sink the ch'i to the tan-tien, the second step is to penetrate the ch'i to the bubbling-well points and the third step is to penetrate the ch'i to the pai hui point.

The highest level, Heaven is an exercise of the functions of perception: It is subdivided into three steps. The first step is to "hear" or try to find out by listening to the energy. The second step is to comprehend the energy. The third step is to arrive at a complete mastery of your opponent. This is a divinely intelligent energy. So there are altogether three levels and nine steps. I will explain them one by one in detail.

The highest level, Heaven is an exercise of the functions of perception.

Man

The method of the first step of Man's level is to relax the sinews from the shoulders to the fingers. If one can relax the sinews, the blood will be naturally active and lively. The process is to relax the sinews of the wrists first, then the elbows and then the shoulders. Without exerting the slightest external muscular force the whole body should be completely relaxed and the movements should be as flexible as possible.

Throughout all the movements there is the straight and bent, which at the same time give the appearance of a circular form. This is the T'ai Chi theory of the square within the circle. However, too much bending or too much straightness are also incorrect. There should be neither deficiency nor excess, neither hollows or projections. In the end you must achieve relaxation from the sinews to the palms of the hands. This is the first step of Man's level.

The second step of Man's level is to relax the sinews from the thighs to the heels of the feet. The processes are the same as the first step but the difference is that the light and heavy, empty and solid must be clearly discriminated. The feet are capable of supporting the whole body's weight. It is different from the movements of the hands which are easy and convenient. Ordinarily we never pay attention to the substantial and insubstantial of the feet and even martial arts boxers let them take their own course.

In T'ai Chi Ch'uan the weight must be put on one foot when the other foot is ready to move forward or backward. It is not allowed to use the slightest muscular force. The thighs, the knees and the heels should be soft and relaxed; the weight should be on the bubbling-well points which are attached to the ground. So the substantial and insubstantial of the feet must be clearly discriminated. It

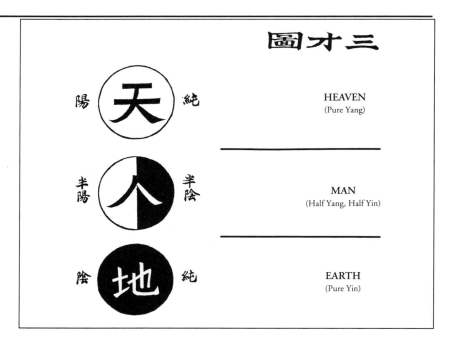

圖才三

HEAVEN
(Pure Yang)

MAN
(Half Yang, Half Yin)

EARTH
(Pure Yin)

San-tsai, the Three
Powers Diagram.

The mind and ch'i abide by the tan-tien and gradually the ch'i will be nourished.

is likewise with the hands. The only difference is that when the right foot is substantial, the right hand must be insubstantial. If this is not the case, it is double-weighting, which should be absolutely avoided from the T'ai Chi point of view. So this is called the second step of Man's level.

The third step of Man's level is to relax the sinews from the lowest vertebrae to the top of the head. The processes are the same as the first step. The spine is the main bone of the body and is its support. It has many joints. It is said that a soft waist will bend as though boneless. From this we can see that the spine must also be flexible. The flexibility of sinews relies upon their softness. The most important thing is that the lowest vertebrae must be plumb erect and the top of the head held as if suspended from above. This is called the third step of Man's level.

Earth

The first step of Earth's level is to sink the ch'i to the tan-tien which is the preliminary foundation for imbibing energy. The tan-tien is situated about 1 1/3 inches below the navel. The tan-tien is found by dividing a horizontal line joining the navel and spine into a ratio of 3:7, measuring from the navel. The mind and ch'i abide by the tan-tien and gradually the ch'i will be nourished. All should be carried out in a natural manner and should not have the slightest forced interpretation.

It is not easy for beginners to learn how to sink the ch'i to the tan-tien. It is necessary to drop the shoulders and lower the elbows. The chest must be slightly concave and the back a little bent. In this way one can cause the ch'i to sink to the tan-tien. Contrary to this, the ch'i will suddenly go up, the shoulders will be raised and the lungs will be lifted up. This manner of holding the body makes it easy for disease to enter.

When the ch'i sinks to the tan-tien it will reach to the four limbs. The ch'i should be directed by the mind so that it will reach the thighs, knees, heels, and the shoulders, elbows and wrists. When the joints of the four limbs are all open, the ch'i can pass downward to the bubbling-well points and upward to the pai hui point and finally to the tips of the middle fingers. The T'ai Chi Classics say, "When the mind directs the ch'i to circulate freely through the whole body, then you can devote oneself to the art of T'ai Chi." This is the second step of the Earth level.

When the ch'i passes over the lowest vertebrae and reaches to the pai hui point, it is called, "passing through three barriers." To pass the ch'i over the lowest vertebrae is the most difficult barrier; the first and second barrier are much easier. When you have practiced T'ai Chi for a long time, according to the correct way, your art will reach a higher level and your ch'i will naturally pass the lowest vertebrae. There should not be the slightest constraint, otherwise it will be in vain and also cause disease. Great caution is to be taken. When the ch'i passes the lowest vertebrae, penetrates into the spine, crosses over the occiput and finally reaches the crown, you have entered the door, that is, you have acquired the correct way of T'ai Chi. It not only can ward off disease and prolong life but is also a short way to achieving Immortality. This is the third step of the Earth level.

*W*hat is energy? How can we hear it? We have to examine these questions minutely.

Heaven

We have to hear the energy. What is energy? How can we hear it? We have to examine these questions minutely. Now let me explain in detail. There is a big difference between energy and force. A secret handed down by the ancient T'ai Chi masters says, "Energy is from the sinews and tendons, whereas, force is from the bones." This saying is indeed true.

It is called energy because the ch'i issued from the sinews and tendons is flexible and elastic. Only by being flexible can you adhere, join, stick to and follow the opponent. By adhering and joining, my ch'i will come in contact with the ch'i of the opponent and so test the motion and tranquility of his ch'i. Therefore, we say "to hear." If your opponent does not move, you do not move. At his slightest stir you have already anticipated it and moved beforehand, taking the opportunity to attack him. This is called the function of sensation. It is the first step of the Heaven level.

We have to understand the energy. The difference between understanding the energy and hearing the energy is like the difference between the deep and shallow and the fine and the coarse. If the opponent stirs only slightly, I can hear it so I move first but to move first I must understand the energy. To obtain a superior posture of your own and to put your opponent in a defective position, this matter rests with yourself and not with your opponent. This is from the shallow to the profound.

It is rather more difficult to describe from coarse to fine. The T'ai Chi classics handed down by the ancient masters say, "When the opponent stirs slightly, I know by hearing it." A slight stir of the opponent's body is easy to examine but if his body does not move, it is hard to understand. If you can hear and know that the opponent is completely still, then you will arrive at a complete mastery of your opponent. This is called, "divine intelligence."

The ch'i from the sinews, veins, membranes and diaphragm is divided into four kinds of energy:

1) defense

2) hidden (latent)

3) ready to issue

4) withdraw and attack

The sinews enable movement of the joints. The veins can circulate the blood. The membranes are attached between the muscles and the flesh and they wrap the bones and sinews. The bowels and viscera are also wrapped by the membranes.

The ch'i from the sinews will not lose its normal attitude. When the ch'i is from the sinews we know that he is going to defend himself. We know that he is going to remain hidden and produce variations when the ch'i is from the veins. When the ch'i is from the diaphragm, that means that he wants to concentrate the energy internally, to withdraw and attack. This is the height of understanding energy. It is ingenious. Nothing compares to it. This is the second step of the Heaven level, "divine intelligence."

If you pay attention to your spirit of vitality and ignore your ch'i, your striking power will be as strong as pure steel.

If you pay attention to your spirit of vitality and ignore your ch'i, your striking power will be as strong as pure steel. If you only pay attention to your ch'i, your blood circulation will be impeded and your striking power will be inactive and inefficient.

When you practice T'ai Chi slowly, effortlessly and continuously, without exerting the slightest external muscular force for a long time, your ch'i will be gradually transformed into spirit of vitality. The issue of the intrinsic energy from the spirit of vitality will be as strong as steel refined a hundred times over. There is no stiff adversary who cannot be overthrown. The ancient T'ai Chi masters could push a person more than thirty feet away without any visible movement of the hands or body and could also knock down a person with any part of their body. This is called supernatural power or divinely intelligent energy.

The T'ai Chi Classics say, "From the mastery of all the postures you will apprehend interpreting energy. From apprehending interpreting energy, you will arrive at a complete mastery of your opponent. Without a long period of arduous practice you cannot find yourself suddenly possessed of this wide and far reaching insight."

Ordinarily we do not see the power in a black cloud passing in the air but if any creature clashes against it, the thunder and lightning hidden in the cloud will immediately burst out. The supernatural power of a T'ai Chi master functions the same way. This is the third step of the Heaven level. You have to ascend step by step and should not skip over any detail.

I wish to follow the mind of Chang San-feng and Wang Chung-yueh and accomplish the unfinished will of these two great T'ai Chi masters. T'ai Chi is the best way to make the race and the nation powerful and productive. I hope all people learning T'ai Chi will exert themselves.

CHAPTER FIVE
WHY I ADOPTED MUSIC TO T'AI CHI CH'UAN

More than one thousand years ago, a Chinese monk named Chan Chung developed a method of concentration during meditation. He told people to repeat silently, "What did I look like before I was born?", that is, "What did I look like when I was in my mother's womb?" Later this method was handed down to Japan as Zen Tao except they use the question, "What is Mu (nothing)?"

We often say that a man's heart is like a monkey, jumping and turning around all the time and his mind is like a horse, galloping without pause. When a man begins to practice meditation, his heart and mind are fully occupied with short thoughts. When one thought is gone, it is immediately replaced by another, giving the heart and mind no chance to rest and concentrate. So monk Chan Chung used his way of concentration to cut out all of the other short, confused thoughts.

As the question, "What did I look like before I was born?" can never be solved, you have to repeat it over and over again for a long time. Gradually your heart and mind will become peaceful and quiet . Only one thing will be left to think of—"What did I look like before I was born?" Finally you will forget even the words you are concentrating on, so your heart and mind will be empty; your body will be completely relaxed; the ch'i will sink and abide by the tan-tien and the blood will circulate through the whole body without hindrance. It is good for health and the way to metamorphose into a Buddha.

It is the same with practicing T'ai Chi. In T'ai Chi the ascent to the highest level is divided into four steps. They are:

A. When beginning the practice of T'ai Chi you will have to memorize the number of beats, the directions, the practical uses of each posture and the ten guiding points. You will breathe naturally and you will not use music.

The Ten Guiding Points, attributed to Yang Cheng-fu,

are as follows:

l) Relax.

2) Sink.

3) Concentrate your line of vision.

4) Hold the chest in, straighten the back, lower the shoulders and elbows.

5) Keep the head upright and the lowest vertebrae plumb erect.

6) Clearly discriminate the substantial and the insubstantial.

7) Direct all the movements by the mind instead of by external muscular force.

8) Be tranquil when you move, be in motion when tranquil.

9) Immediately follow up with down and down with up; move the whole body as one unit.

10) Connect all the movements without severance.

B. After you have attained a degree of mastery of the things mentioned

We often say that a man's heart is like a monkey, jumping and turning around all the time and his mind is like a horse, galloping without pause.

above, you will begin to use the beats, music, and proper breathing (methods of inhaling and exhaling). The rest you will forget.

C. At the next stage you will use only the music for concentration.

D. After practicing T'ai Chi with music for a sufficient length of time, you will forget the music, the movements and even yourself, although you will proceed as usual. At this stage you will be in a trance and your five attributes: form, perception, consciousness, action and knowledge, will be empty. This is complete relaxation of the body and mind. It is very good for health and the way to immortality.

Of course, if you can reach the highest level while practicing T'ai Chi without music, so much the better. I cannot do it because I am a human being, an ordinary, ignorant person with a heart like a monkey and mind like a horse. I must use music as a means of concentration, as a stepping stone to the highest level of T'ai Chi.

I like music, especially soft music. I believe it is in a human being's nature. It can relieve tension and anxiety, produce happiness and relaxation and increase harmony and coordination.

During the forty years I have practiced T'ai Chi to music, I have taught in many universities, colleges and high schools. I have had thousands of students study with me. They have said that T'ai Chi with music is more enjoyable than without it. T'ai Chi with music has value and is not extraneous to the essence of T'ai Chi Ch'uan. If it was, I would not be eighty-six years of age and enjoying perfect health. I like music and have chosen to continue practicing T'ai Chi to music to maintain my good health.

At this stage you will be in a trance and your five attributes: form, perception, consciousness, action and knowledge, will be empty.

CHAPTER SIX
A LECTURE BY PROFESSOR CHENG MAN-CH'ING
Recorded by T.T. Liang

T'ai Chi is both a physical exercise and an art of self-defense, invented by the Taoist, Chang San-feng, five centuries ago. In this exercise you have to breathe naturally and relax every muscle in your body. This will help to circulate the ch'i and blood. Your posture and movements will remain in complete balance. The main object is to prevent illness, to lengthen life and to strengthen your body and mind. If this stage is accomplished you can study the self-defence aspects. Even if someone hits me with great force, I have no fear of him because I can overcome him.

When I first learned T'ai Chi Ch'uan, its original procedure consisted of 128 postures. This series required more than ten minutes to go through. To save time, I cut off the repeated motions and deleted the similar ones to get thirty-six postures. These postures preserve the essence of the original postures. Practicing this form fast requires only three minutes; practicing it slow will take five minutes. If you practice it once each morning and evening, it takes only ten minutes to complete.

I. The General Principles of Exercise.

There are only two reasons for exercise. It is either for the body, or for its practical use. In order to realize these objectives, you must consider the following six elements: (l) the duration of practice, (2) the degree of attainment, (3) the difference in energy used, (4) the range of changes, (5) the skill of application, and (6) the speed of comprehension. These six elements depend upon proper instruction, natural talent, and perseverance. Of the three conditions, the first and third are similarly important. Without proper instruction, you will not be successful, even with natural talent and perseverance. Even if you possesses natural talent and have good instruction, if you cannot persevere, it will be difficult to acquire the art.

The Classics say, "Sink the ch'i (breath) to the tan-tien (the pubic region) and spread it throughout the body. Operate ch'i by the will and operate the body by the ch'i so the bones become permeated with it." An advanced practitioner will be able to throttle their breath (ch'i) down to the softness of a child's breath. This kind of attainment comes from the accumulation of ch'i which in turn enables an accumulation of strength. The energy produced will be inestimable. It all depends upon the method of instruction and the depth of knowledge.

How do you proceed to learn? The primary requirement is relaxation. You have to relax the body completely and thoroughly so that the ch'i can run through the joints and muscles freely. With regards to ch'i, it has to be sunk to the tan-tien first. To do this, the chest has to be kept open in order to let the ch'i sink down and gradually accumulate. This is the beginning of the accumulation of ch'i. That is called exercise. Exercise must be set in operation first before it is in motion. An automobile or steamboat must be operated by steam

An advanced practitioner will be able to throttle their breath (ch'i) down to the softness of a child's breath.

Professor Cheng
Man-ch'ing

When there is ample ch'i in the tan-tien, the skin will become tougher and therefore, able to resist impact.

first before it can move. So the movements of hands and feet must first be mobilized by ch'i.

II. The Physical Principles.

Statements in the classics say, "Keep the coccyx upright and centered so as to make your spirit pass upward to the top of the head. Having the head in an upright position, as if hanging in the air, will result in the whole body being light and comfortable." These statements discuss the main method of exercising the spinal column. If the head is hung on a beam it cannot move in any direction. The spinal column is strengthened because the spinal column from the coccyx upward to the head is controlled. Strengthening of the spinal column not only gives more strength to the viscera inside the body but also makes the brain more efficient. This is the function of repairing your bodily essence.

Next in importance is the sinking of the ch'i to the tan-tien. The tan-tien is a technical term used by the Taoists. It means symbolically a piece of land in which seeds are sown for the purpose of creating a sort of nutritious element called "tan" or elixir of immortality. Its position is beneath the navel by 1.3 inches, nearer to the navel than to the spine in a proportion of 3 to 7. If your ch'i is abundant in the tan-tien the membranes of the whole body will be strengthened. A membrane is just like the inner tube of a tire. When there is ample ch'i in the tan-tien, the skin will become tougher and therefore, able to resist impact.

III. The Principles of Application.

The application of T'ai Chi Ch'uan depends upon understanding the essence of the principles. The necessity of "getting the chance and seizing the condition" and the application of "using four ounces of strength to ward off one thousand pounds of impact" teach you to defend yourself with understanding rather than brute strength. Fighting originally relied upon the use of technique coupled with strength and aggression. Having no aggression and no strength, technique alone accomplished nothing.

But the idea of T'ai Chi Ch'uan is contrary to the usual concept. Both strength and aggression have to be abandoned. T'ai Chi requires, "a flexible body in any movement" and for the motion to be so exact that, "a feather cannot be added to it and a fly cannot alight on it without setting it in motion."

The classics also tell the novice, "Abandon yourself and follow your opponent." Isn't it strange to learn to abandon yourself and to follow your opponent as a means of defense? For instance, when someone hits me with great impact, how can I yield myself and follow him? Such a thing seems to be unbelievable. When I am hit with a powerful impact, I do not hit back but also do not resist his strike. However, I do not accept his strike either but send the impact back by following his striking force. In this way my opponent will fall down by the impact of his own strength. This is the way of creating the opportunity and warding off one thousand pounds of impact by the application of four ounces of my pull. It is derived from the principle of abandoning yourself to follow the opponent. The principle has to be understood figuratively. It does not mean that in reality you use a thing of four ounces to push back an impact of one thousand pounds.

The exercise the novice should begin with is tui shou. In this form of exercise you should follow the principle of four words: adhering, joining, touching, and following. Adhering means to stick together. Joining means not to let the hands fall apart. These two words point to the upward and downward movements. The other two words apply to the forward and backward and the right and left movements.

In this exercise we are told, "not to abandon, nor push back violently." Not to abandon means not to resist the attack of the opponent. The hands of the opposing parties are pushing in circular motion by repetition, just like the inseparability of shadow from body or echo from sound. When this form of exercise has been practiced for a long time you can leave the applied energy to rotate by itself, coming or going, ebbing or waning, increasing or decreasing, reinforcing and withdrawing and yielding or resisting. If such variations are felt, then the student can be said to have gained the primary principle of the technique. Through continual practice one will gradually comprehend the idea of applied energy and will have reached the advanced stage.

IV. How Can the Roots of the Opponent Be Pulled Up?

In tui shou, when energy is issued, it is most effective if the two heels of the opponent can be pulled up. If only the front part of the opponent's feet are pulled up, the method of pulling up and letting down is not accurate enough. To be able to pull up the opponent's two heels, the following six essentials should be observed:

1. The classics say, "The root is your feet and the energy is sent out through the legs, controlled by the hips and operated by the fingers. From the feet upward through the legs to the hips, the movement should be executed as one

The hands of the opposing parties are pushing in circular motion by repetition, just like the inseparability of shadow from body or echo from sound.

whole." The idea is that when an energy is sent out, you should stand with the hips slightly backward as if in a sitting posture. This will make use of the elasticity of the back part of the thighs and hold the hips in the right position. The energy sent out should have the tendency to raise something upward. The elasticity of the back part of the thighs is shifted to the front, to make the energy go into the ground, where the man stands. The bent knees should not project beyond the toes. If they do, the energy issued will become loose.

Only with square shoulders, downward extending arms, a straight spinal column and an upright head can the whole body's energy be sent out in unison so that any root can be pulled up. If some slight deviation arises in a certain part, the energy will be greatly reduced.

2. When both hands touch the body of the opponent, the strength applied should never be too much, otherwise it will be felt by the opponent who will try to neutralize it. It will then be impossible to pull up his root.

3. When both hands touch the opponent's body, it is better to be able to feel the wavering in him. It is most effective to issue your energy at the moment of the wavering signs of the opponent although it is difficult to feel the wavering of the opponent's body . This has to be learned by hard work in "tui shou" exercise.

When issuing your energy, never do it with both hands simultaneously.

4. When issuing your energy, never do it with both hands simultaneously. If energy is sent out simultaneously by both hands, it is a double application. The classics say, "Energy should be issued only on one side." So, application by both hands at the same time is contrary to the principle of one-sided application. It will be better to issue energy through one hand, with the other hand ready to help.

5. The distance between the body and the hands should remain unchanged before and after the sending out of energy. If, in issuing energy, the hands either stretch out or withdraw, it will influence the application of energy from your body in unison and decrease the effect of pulling up the root.

6. When issuing energy, both hips and thighs should be kept relaxed in a sitting position. Then, when the energy is actually being sent out, the body changes to a rising position to make the pulling up work possible. The classics say, "If you intend to rise up you should have the idea of sitting down. If you intend to lift a thing up, you should apply energy pushing it down first to shake the roots, so that they will break off by themselves." This is the very idea.

V. My Interpretation.

Man has to have physical exercise. *The Book of Change (I Ching)* says, "The movement of heaven is full of power. Thus the superior man makes himself strong and untiring." That is the foundation of making yourself strong. For the same reason, "a door pivot never gets worm eaten and running water never becomes putrid." However, there are many ways of exercise. You have to make a choice. Some like weight lifting, wrestling, or running; others like playing ball, skating, swimming, boxing or fencing. Each man has his own taste. But none of them can get away from the principle of using strength and competing for speed.

This does not apply to T'ai Chi Ch'uan. This form of exercise can be learned by the sick, the old and the young because it does not require the use of much strength, nor does it require speed. If it is practiced by youth or adults it will not have the effect of promoting inappropriate fighting or the desire to over-power others. It can be enjoyed in any kind of weather, rain or shine, hot or cold. It can be practiced in any kind of environment, regardless of your profession. You cannot be injured as in skating or swimming. It requires little strenuous work as is required in boxing, wrestling and fencing. Only an area of three square feet and a short interval of seven minutes is required. So long as you have the mind to learn, you do not have to spend a cent to perform the exercise.

This form of exercise can be learned by the sick, the old and the young because it does not require the use of much strength.

CHAPTER SEVEN
The 150 Posture Solo Form

The following instructions for these 150 postures were taken from Master Liang's original notes which he composed more than ten years prior to this printing. In some cases there are a few minor variations concerning the execution of a posture. Ten years have passed and like all things there has occurred change. These variations, however are neither frequent nor drastic enough to summon detailed comment here. Besides, the purpose of this work is not to decide nor argue at which time in Master Liang's career he was more correct in his teachings, as that would be a great error in itself. Therefore, it was decided to present the instructions as Master Liang originally composed them. Otherwise I fear misinterpretation because everyone, myself included, sees the same thing a little differently.

About the Photographs

For the first time ever this book presents stop-motion photography of T'ai Chi Ch'uan movements. These photos help the reader understand and visualize to a greater extent the full range of motion undertaken during the performance of each posture. Additionally each posture is divided into counts, and each of those counts within the postures is also shown photographically. Finally, photographs are given of Master Liang performing the last movement of the posture.

With the three series of photographs, along with the written explanation, the movements of T'ai Chi Ch'uan can be more easily imitated and learned. But even moreso, these photographs truly preserve, for the first time, Master Liang's 150 Posture T'ai Chi Ch'uan Solo Form.

			I CHING SYMBOL CHART		
Image	Name	Symbol		Attributes	T'ai Chi Posture
☰	*Ch'ien*	Heaven		*Strength/Creativity*	Ward-Off
☷	*K'un*	Earth		*Passive/Receptivity*	Roll-Back
☵	*K'an*	Water		*Danger/Difficulty*	Press
☲	*Li*	Fire		*Brightness/Wisdom*	Push
☳	*Chen*	Thunder		*Motion/Vibration*	Split
☴	*Sun*	Wind/Wood		*Pliancy/Pentetration*	Pull
☶	*Ken*	Mountain		*Firmness/Obstruction*	Shoulder-Stroke
☱	*Tui*	Lake		*Gentleness/Grace*	Elbow-Stroke

About the I-Ching Symbols

T'ai Chi Ch'uan is primarily based on two early and profound
Chinese philosophies, the *I-Ching* and the *Tao Te Ching*. The *I-Ching
(Book of Changes)* deals with the fluctuations of yin and yang, forming
sixty-four basic images or hexagrams. The postures of T'ai Chi Ch'uan
are each represented by one of these hexagrams and they are included
here to show the connection.

Master Liang's arrangement of the postures does not always conform
with the natural progression of these images. So here we have more of
a patchwork than a linear progression. In a later book we will be show-
ing how the T'ai Chi Ch'uan postures should be arranged to conform
to the progression of the hexagram images, and explaining how the
philosophy of the I-Ching and Tao Te Ching influenced the art of
T'ai Chi Ch'uan. For now I hope that the inclusion of these images
will stimulate your interest in the philosophical roots of T'ai Chi
Ch'uan.

無
極

WU CHI

Wu Chi

Before actually beginning the movements of T'ai Chi you stand in the Wu Chi posture. This posture, however, is not counted as one of the 150 postures of the form itself because there is no movement; yin and yang have not yet separated. The principles of this posture are as follows:

— Suspend the head as if by a thread from above.

— Gaze levelly to the front.

— Lower the shoulders.

— Hollow the chest.

— Hold the spine erect.

— Hang the arms downward and loosely along the sides of the body.

— Draw in the buttocks.

— Sink the ch'i to the tan-tien.

—Bend the knees slightly (do not lock the knee joints).

—With heels of both feet touching separate the toes to form a "V" shape with the feet.

—Place the tongue on the roof of the mouth, lightly close the teeth and lips and stand quietly until all the tension in the body disappears.

Wu Chi in translation means, "that which is without limit" or "the Illimitable." According to Chinese philosophy Wu Chi is where all things are produced and T'ai Chi is the product. This term was first introduced by the Taoist, Chou Tun-yi, of the Sung dynasty as a philosophical theory of a mind without thought or desire, hence, a mind without limit.

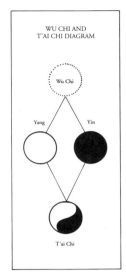

Posture 1 豫
備
式

YU PEI SHIH

PREPARATION POSTURE

During the counts of:

1. Shift your weight completely onto the right leg. Raise the left foot and place it sideways about twelve inches to the left, toes pointing directly ahead (north) and rest your weight on it; at the same time bend the elbows slightly outward with the palms facing backward. 100R-0L

2. Pivoting on the right heel, raise the right toes and curve them slightly inward so that the right foot is parallel to the left foot. Both feet are now pointing directly ahead (north). The weight is centered between the two legs; the distance between the feet should be equal to the distance between the shoulders; the shoulders should always be slumped, the chest depressed, with the tongue resting against the hard palate and the mouth lightly closed. The spine should be as straight as possible, the lowest vertebrae hanging in a plumbline with the head floating as though suspended from above. The entire body should be relaxed completely. It is only then that the ch'i can sink to the tan-tien (one and one-third inches below the navel). 50R-50L

Weight Distribution Notation:
At the end of each description of a particular count you will find
an indication for the correct weight distribution at the completion
of the count. For example, 70R-30L will mean that seventy percent
of your weight is on the right leg and thirty percent on your left.

Posture 2 起勢

CH'I SHIH

CHIN

Advancement

Fire Over Earth

During the counts of:

1. Looking forward, inhaling slowly, gradually raise the arms forward and upwards to shoulder height with wrists bent and fingers hanging down. 50R-50L

2. Slowly extend the fingers so that they point forward (north). 50R-50L

3. Bend the elbows slightly and allow the hands to float upwards to a 45 degree angle. 50R-50L

4. Lower the elbows slightly downward. 50R-50L

5. Slowly lower your hands (wrists sinking as though supported by water) until they are below the hip joints with palms facing backward. 50R-50L

6. Bend the elbows slightly forward and outward with the thumbs lightly touching the side of the hips. Let the fingers hang downward. 50R-50L

Posture 3　　左
　　　　　掤

TSO P'ENG

CH'IEN
The Creative
Heaven Over Heaven

During the counts of:

1. Shift the weight to the left leg and allowing the knees to bend slightly, gradually turn the trunk about 45 degrees to the right (northeast). 20R-80L

2. Continue to turn the trunk 45 degrees to the right (east). The toes of the right foot rise up slightly and the foot pivots on the heel to the right (east) so that it is now at a right angle to the left foot. Throughout the turning of the trunk, the legs and arms must be allowed to move simultaneously with the waist and hips. Keep the elbow slightly down while simultaneously raising the right hand gradually, palm down, to the level of the armpit and slowly bring the left hand, palm up, to the level of the right waist. (Note: The arm movement actually begins on Count #1.) Feel as though a large ball of air were being held between the hands. The eyes have accompanied this movement and are now looking directly ahead (east). 0R-100L

3. Shift the majority of the weight to the right foot. 60R-40L

4. Gradually turn the trunk about 45 degrees to the left (northeast) so that the left foot is brought to the tip of the toes. 100R-0L

5. Touching first with the heel, place the left foot directly forward and slowly shift the weight onto it while turning the upper torso to the left. At the same time raise the left arm with the elbow slightly down. Lower the right arm while pivoting on the heel, turning the right foot inward so that the toes point northeast. 40R-60L

6. Shift 70 percent of your weight to the left foot; simultaneously continue to raise the left arm until the palm of the hand faces your chest and continue to lower the right arm until the hand rests beside the right hip joint, palm backward. The eyes have accompanied this gradual turning movement and now look directly ahead (north). 30R-70L

Posture 4 右掤

YU P'ENG

CH'IEN

The Creative

Heaven Over Heaven

During the counts of:

1. Shift most of the weight to the left leg and turn the trunk slowly toward the right (northeast). 20R-80L

2. Continue to turn the trunk to the right (east) until the right foot is brought to its toe (pointing east); at the same time gradually turn the palms of the hands so that they face each other. 0R-100L

3. Raise the toes off the ground and place the right foot down heel first on the same spot previously occupied by the toes and gradually shift the weight to the foot. At the same time pivot on the left heel and stretching the left leg, slightly turn the left foot inward (northeast). Shift 70 percent of the body weight to the bent right leg. At the same time the right arm, with elbow slightly lowered, is carried upwards until the palm faces the upper chest. The left arm, elbow down, moves towards the east until the palm of the hand faces outward with the fingers pointing upwards midway between the upper chest and the right hand. Feel again that a ball of air is being held with the left hand on the near side of the ball and the right hand on the far side of it; the diameter of the ball being about six inches. You are now facing northeast. 60R-40L

4. Sink downward slightly. 70R-30L

Posture 5 擾

LU

K'UN

The Receptive

Earth Over Earth

During the counts of:

1. Gradually turn the torso rightward (to face southeast). At the same time extend the right arm slightly, bending the elbow downward so that the fingers point upwards with the palm facing northeast. Bend the left elbow slightly downward so that the left hand, palm faces in, is held near the chest at the level of the right elbow (for protection). 80R-20L

2. Gradually turn the torso to the left (to face east). The body and the hands are to act as one unit. 80R-20L

3. Slowly sink the weight of the body onto the left foot. 40R-60L

4. Bend the left knee to allow the left leg to bear the full weight of the body as the torso turns to the left (northeast). At the same time turn your left palm slightly upward in order to disperse your opponent's "push energy." This posture is the epitome of the "yield" required in T'ai Chi Ch'uan and it must be done correctly. You are now facing northeast. 20R-80L

Posture 6

CHI

K'AN
Perilous Water
Water Over Water

During the counts of:

1. Turn the torso slightly to the left (to face north); let the left hand trace a clockwise circle backward, upward and then forward. 0R-100L

2. Turn the body gradually to the right (east), with the right arm, elbow bent and palm of the hand facing the upper chest. Lightly rest the fingers of the left hand upon the inner wrist of the right hand. 20R-80L

3. Gradually shift the weight onto the right leg. 60R-40L

4. Rise off the rear leg with the hands and body as one unit until the right leg bears 70 percent of the weight. Thus the hands are advanced upwards by the body. You are now facing east. 70R-30L

Posture 7   按

AN

LI
Adhering Light
Fire Over Fire

During the counts of:

1. Separate your hands, palms down, at the level of your shoulders with arms slightly stretched and sink slightly into the front leg. 80R-20L

2. Withdraw your body backward until the weight of the entire body is shifted onto the left leg. As the arms are withdrawn, the elbows hang down and the palms of the hands face downward with the wrists at the level of the shoulders. 20R-80L

3. Shift your weight onto the right, without unbending the rear leg. 60R-40L

4. Rise up off the rear leg and root into the front leg. The hands simultaneously rise upwards until the palms face outwards. 70R-30L

Posture 8

單
鞭

TAN PIEN

KO
Revolution
Lake Over Fire

During the counts of:

1. Shift your weight gradually back onto the left foot with the palms of the hands facing downward and hands parallel with the shoulders. 20R-80L

2. Turn your torso to the left until it faces north and at the same time swivel on the right heel, curving the toes inward to the north. 0R-100L

3. As the weight is shifted back to the right leg, allow the body to turn to the right (so that it will be facing northeast) and as the elbow bends withdraw the right arm. Allow the fingers to point downward and close together at the fingertips, thus forming a "hook" near the right armpit. Bring the left hand to rest, palm up, near the right rib area. 80R-20L

4. As the torso turns gradually leftward (to face the northeast corner) and swivels on the ball of the left foot so that the toes point northwest extend the "hook" hand rightward so that the knuckles face the northwest corner. 100R-0L

5. As the trunk continues to turn leftward, take a wide step across and out to the west with the left foot. First set the heel down, shift the weight to the leg. The left heel should not be directly in front of the right heel but on as wide a diagonal position as can be comfortably managed. At the same time turn the right foot inward maintaining contact on the floor with the heel. The left hand, palm turning inward, is carried leftward until it is opposite the left shoulder. Throughout this movement the eyes gaze at the palm of the hand. 40R-60L

6. Gradually sink 70 percent of the body weight to the left leg, bending the leg at the knee. At the same time turn the left hand palm outward with the arm slightly bent and look past the fingertips. You are now facing west. 30R-70L

Posture 9

提
手

T'I SHOU

PI
Gracefulness
Mountain Over Fire

During the counts of:

1. Shift the weight onto the right leg and turn in the left foot slightly (20 degrees). Then shift all your weight back to your left leg. Turn your palms inward so that they face each other. 0R-100L

2. Carry your right foot leftward until you can place the heel (toes pointing up) on the ground about a foot's length in front of your left heel. At the same time slowly bring your arms toward each other so that your right elbow is slightly bent and aligned over your right leg in advance of your left arm. Your left arm, elbow slightly bent, has the palm facing the crook of the right elbow shoulder width apart. The hands and the legs must move and stop at the same time. As it says in the T'ai Chi Ch'uan classics, "When you act, everything moves and when you stand still, everything is tranquil." You are now facing north. 0R-100L

Posture 10

K'AO

TA CHUANG

Great Strength

Thunder Over Heaven

During the counts of:

1. Bring your right foot back and place it down on the toes of the foot with the toes directly in front of your left heel. At the same time retract and lower your right hand and let it hang, palm inward so that the outer edge of the hand is near the front of your right thigh. Lower your left hand and let it hang, palm outward, so that its outer edge is near the outer left thigh. 0R-100L

2. Step forward with your right foot (heel touching first) and shift 70 percent of your weight to it. Lightly apply your left hand to the crook of your right forearm. 70R-30L

Posture 11

白
鶴
亮
翅

PAI HAO LIANG CH'IH

TUI

Joyousness

Lake Over Lake

During the counts of:

1. Shift your weight back to the left foot and turn your right foot slightly inward (20 degrees). Shift all your weight to your right foot as you turn leftward (to face northwest). Begin to raise your right arm, tracing about 90 degrees of a large clockwise circle, and begin to lower your left arm. The right hand moves upward and inside of the left arm. 100R-0L

2. Bring your left foot forward (along a diagonally right line) and place only its toes down so that they are in alignment with your right heel . At the same time raise your right arm until your right elbow hangs at the level of your chin and your right hand (palm forward, fingers pointing upward) is above your head. Continue to lower your left arm until the hand rests beside your left hip joint, its palm facing backward. You are now facing west. 100R-0L

Posture 12

左
摟
膝
拗
步

TSO LOU HSIH YAO PU

KU

Deterioration

Mountain Over Wind

BRUSH LEFT KNEE AND TWIST STEP

During the counts of:

1. Lower the body on a slightly bended right knee. At the same time your right hand, palm up, is to be turned and lowered beside the right side. 100R-0L

2. Continue to turn the trunk to the right facing northwest, and with the right hand circle in a counter-clockwise path: backward, upward and forward until the palm comes beside the right ear, facing forward (west), elbow bent. Continue circling the left hand until it faces the right side of the chest with the fingers pointing north. The left arm forms a bow shape and the palm turns inward to face the body. 100R-0L

3. Gradually turn the body to the left (west). Take a step diagonally forward (left) with the left foot, heel touching the ground first, and brush the left knee with the left hand, palm facing backwards; let it rest (stop) beside the left thigh. Bring the right arm, elbow bent, in front of the chest. At the same time gradually shift the weight to the left foot and rotating on the right heel, turn your right foot slightly inward. 40R-60L

4. Gradually shift 70 percent of the body weight to the left foot and using the intrinsic energy of the entire body, push off the rear leg along with the right hand, elbow slightly bent. You are still facing west. 30R-70L

Posture 13 手揮琵琶

SHOU HUI P'I PA

SUI
Following
Lake Over Thunder

During the counts of:

1. Pick up your right foot, turn it 20 degrees to the right, set it down and shift the entire body weight to it. Turn the right palm inward as you shift weight. 100R-0L

2. Bring your left foot slightly sideways to the right and touch the ground with the heel only, which should be in line with the right heel. At the same time bring the right hand along in a backward arc, palm facing south, and carry it to a position opposite the left elbow, raising the left hand, palm facing north, so that the fingers are in line with the mouth. The elbow is slightly bent and the fingers point west. The position simulates playing a guitar. You are still facing west. 100R-0L

Posture 14　左摟膝拗步

TSO LOU HSIH YAO PU

KU

Deterioration

Mountain Over Wind

BRUSH LEFT KNEE AND TWIST STEP   Posture 14

During the counts of:

1. This count is the same as posture #12, count 1 except that the left foot drops but no weight is placed on it, while the right arm and hand stay extended from the previous posture. 100R-0L

Counts 2, 3, and 4 are the same as the respective counts of posture #12.

Posture 15

右
摟
膝
拗
步

YU LOU HSIH YAO PU

CHIEN

Gradual Progress

Wood Over Mounain

During the counts of:

1. Withdraw the body weight to the right foot and turn the torso slightly to the left, turning the left toes slightly outward on the feet to point southwest. At the same time the right hand is brought leftward until the palm faces inward. 100R-0L

2. Shift the body weight to the left foot and circle the left hand clockwise, backward, upward, and forward to the left ear. This palm should be facing outward and slightly inclined downward with this elbow bent. The right arm forms a bow and the palm turns to face the body. 0R-100L

3. Turn the torso slightly to the right and take a big step forward with the right foot, heel touching the ground first. Brush the right knee with the right hand, palm backward, bringing it to rest beside the right thigh. Begin shifting the body weight to the right foot and curve the left foot slightly inward, turning on the heel. 60R-40L

4. When 70 percent of the body weight is on the right foot, with the intrinsic energy of your entire body push the left hand forward, with the elbow slightly bent. You are still facing west. 70R-30L

Posture 16

左
摟
膝
拗
步

TSO LOU HSIH YAO PU

KU

Deterioration

Mountain Over Wind

During the counts of:

1. As the body weight is withdrawn onto the left foot, turn the torso slightly to the right and turn the right foot slightly outward so that it points northwest. At the same time turn the left hand so that the palm faces inward. 0R-100L

2. Shift the body weight to the right foot and circle the right hand counterclockwise from downward to upward until it is by the right ear, palm facing forward and slightly inclined, with the elbow bent downward. The right arm forms a bow and the palm turns to face the body. 100R-0L

Counts 3 and 4 are the same as the respective counts of posture #12.

Posture 17 手揮琵琶

PLAYING THE GUITAR
This posture is the same as posture #13.

SUI
Following
Lake Over Thunder

左
摟
膝
拗
步

BRUSH LEFT KNEE AND TWIST STEP

During the counts of:

1.This count is the same as posture #12, count 1 except that the left foot drops but no weight is placed on it. Counts 2, 3, and 4 are the same as the respective counts of posture #12.

KU

Deterioration

Mountain Over Wind

Posture 19

搬
身
捶

P'IEH SHEN CH'UI

TING
The Cauldron
Fire Over Wood

During the counts of:

1. Draw the body back to shift the weight to your right foot and pivot on your left heel to turn the raised foot slightly outward, pointing southwest; lower the right hand leftward until the palm faces the left thigh. 100R-0L

2. Shift 70 percent of the body weight to the left foot; turn the body slightly to the right (northwest) and at the same time clench your right hand into a fist and chop upward in a forward direction toward the northwest. The knuckles are downward at the height of your nose. Raise your left hand backward until it rests at the height of the waist, palm down. You are now facing northwest and looking at your right fist. 30R-70L

Posture 20 進步搬攔捶

CHIN PU PAN LAN CH'UI

YU

Happiness

Thunder Over Earth

STEP FORWARD, DEFLECT DOWNWARD, INTERCEPT AND PUNCH

During the counts of:

1. Withdraw the weight of your right foot, turn the torso slightly to the left, facing southwest and raise the left toes. At the same time open the right fist, turn the hand palm down, and lower it near your left waist; lower the left hand, palm up, close to the left hip joint. 100R-0L

2. Shift the weight to the left foot. 40R-60L

3. Raise the right foot and take a short step diagonally to the forward right direction with only the heel touching the ground. At the same time make a fist with the right hand, with knuckles down, and bring it back to rest under the right side of the waist (deflect); raise the left hand and circle it clockwise, backward, upward and forward near the left ear with the elbow bent and palm facing west. 0R-100L

4. As you sink the body downward, shift the weight to your right foot and let the left hand move forward and downward to be held in front of your right chest with palm down to intercept. 60R-40L

5. Step forward with the left foot and gradually shift 60 percent of the weight to it; extend the left hand forward and leftward, fingers pointing west and the palm facing north. Curve your right foot slightly inward. Draw the right fist back alongside the right hip, with palm facing up. 40R-60L

6. Shift 70 percent of the body weight to the left foot and punch forward with the right fist, with tiger's mouth upward ("tiger's mouth" is the space between the crook of the index finger and thumb). Draw back the left hand so that it slides past the advancing right fist and comes to rest on the inside of the inner wrist of the right hand. You are now facing west. 30R-70L

Posture 21

如
封
似
開

JU FENG SHIH PI

CHIA JEN
The Family
Wind Over Fire

During the counts of:

1. Gradually withdraw the body, sinking the weight to the right foot, and open the right fist so that the palm is upward. Turn the left palm upward and slide it under the right hand. 20R-80L

2. Continue to shift the weight back until all of it is on the right foot; draw both hands back close to the chest and separate the hands turning the palms outward with elbows bent. 80R-20L

3. Shift the weight on to the left foot. 40R-60L

4. Rise off the rear leg and root into the front leg. The hands simultaneously rise upwards until the palms face outwards. 30R-70L

Posture 22 十字手

SHIH TSU SHOU

MING YI
Darkened Light
Earth Over Fire

During the counts of:

1. Gradually sink the body weight onto the right leg and slightly stretch the arms forward with palms downward. 80R-20L

2. Begin turning the body to the right (north), pivoting on the left heel until the foot moving inward points north. Let the right hand be carried along the upward arc of a high circle, with the left hand guided by the turning waist, following the right hand along the same trajectory. 100R-0L

3. As all the body weight is shifted to the left foot, pivot on the right toes to turn the right heel inward and gradually lower both hands in opposite directions and down the sides of the circle (right hand, clockwise), (left hand, counterclockwise). 0R-100L

4. Bring the right foot back and place it parallel to the left foot, shoulder width apart, so that both feet point directly ahead (north); the knees are slightly bent and the weight of the body is mostly on the left foot.

As the hands approach each other along the lower arc of the circle, cross them diagonally at the wrists and bring them up in front of the chest, palms facing you with the right wrist outside the left wrist. You are now facing north. 30R-70L

Posture 23 抱虎歸山

PAO HU KUEI SHAN

KEN
Resting
Mountain Over Mountain

During the counts of:

1. Gradually turn your body to the right (northeast) and turn your right palm down and your left palm up. At the same time turn your right heel slightly leftward with toes touching the ground. 100R-0L

2. Continue to turn your body to the right and take a step with your right foot to the far right (southeast) with the heel touching first. At the same time lower both hands and together with the right foot move the right hand towards the southeast with the palm outward, and circle the left hand clockwise in a backwards direction, palm up. 0R-100L

3. Continue to move your right hand rightward and backward and place it beside your right thigh with palm upward. The left hand makes a clockwise circle downward, backward and upward; it stops past the left ear to the front of the body with palm forward and elbow bent. Turn your left foot slightly inward, pivoting on the heel and shift 60 percent of the weight to the right foot. 60R-40L

4. Shift 70 percent of your weight to the right foot. With the intrinsic energy of your whole body, push your left hand forward (southeast) without bending the wrist and with the fingers diagonally upward. You are now facing southeast. 70R-30L

Posture 24 擴

ROLL-BACK

This posture is the same as posture #5, except:

1. Face south.

K'UN

2. Face southeast.

The Receptive

3. Face southeast.

Earth Over Earth

4. Face east.

PRESS

This posture is the same as posture #6, except:

1. Face northeast.
2. Face southeast.
3. Face southeast.
4. Face southeast.

T'UNG JEN

Togetherness

Heaven Over Fire

Posture 26 按

PUSH

This posture is the same as posture #7, except:

1. Face southeast.

TA YU   2. Face southeast.

Great Wealth   3. Face southeast.

Fire Over Heaven   4. Face southeast.

斜
單
鞭

SLANTING SINGLE WHIP

This posture is the same as posture #8, except:

1. Face southeast.
2. Face northeast.
3. Face southeast.
4. Face northeast.
5. Face northwest.
6. Face northwest.

CHUNG FU
Inner Truth
Wind Over Lake

Posture 28 肘底看捶

CHOU TI CH'UI

YI
Nourishment
Mountain Over Thunder

During the counts of:

1. Shift your weight back to your right leg.

2. Turn your body to the left and take one step to the left with your left foot, with toes pointing west. At the same time open the right hand "hook". 100R-0L

3. Shift the weight to the left foot. 40R-60L

4. Bring your right foot to the forward right direction on a line north of your left heel and with the toes pointing northwest. Shift your weight to your right leg, immediately turn your upper torso further to the left (south) with your arms evenly extended on either side, with palms downward. 100R-0L

5. When you have turned your upper torso as far as you can (facing south) and your right hand (extended toward the west) is opposite your left shoulder, start to lower your left hand and circle it downward to the right and upward from beneath your right forearm. At the same time turn your upper torso to the right. 100R-0L

6. Continue to circle your left hand up and inside the right forearm until the fingers are pointing almost vertically upward. At the same time take a one-half step with your left foot diagonally to the front center, with only the heel touching and in line with your right heel. Make a fist with your right hand ("tiger's mouth" facing up) and bring it to where the "tiger's mouth" sits just beneath the left elbow. You are now facing west. 100R-0L

Posture 29　倒攆猴右式

TAO NIEN HOU YU SHIH

TUN

Retreat

Heaven Over Mountain

During the counts of:

1. Turn your body to the right (facing north) and opening your right fist, palm up, circle your right hand counterclockwise, downward, backward and upward and extend it toward the east at shoulder height. At the same time turn your left hand, palm down, and extend it to the front (west) at shoulder height. 100R-0L

2. Turn your body to the left (to face west) and continue to circle your right hand by bringing it forward and place it beside your right ear with the palm forward and slightly downward. 100R-0L

3. Turn your left hand palm upward and draw it back and downward and put it beside your left thigh. Draw the right hand downward, with the elbow bent, in front of the chest with the fingers pointing slightly upwards. At the same time step back with your left foot with toes pointing directly west and shift the weight to it and curve your toes slightly inward. 40R-60L

4. Sinking the weight to your left foot, simultaneously push the right hand forward with the elbow slightly bent and the palm outward. You are still facing west. 20R-80L

Posture 30

倒攆猴 左式

TAO NIEN HOU TSO SHIH

SUN

Decrease

Mountain Over Lake

During the counts of:

1. Turn your body to the left (to face south) and circle your left hand downward, backward and upward to extend it eastward at shoulder height with palm upward. Extend your right hand toward the west with palm downward. 0R-100L

2. Turn your body to the right (to face west) and bending your left arm, shift your left hand beside your left ear, with palm forward and slightly downward. 0R-100L

3. Turn your right hand, palm up, and draw it back and downward and put it beside your right thigh. Draw the left hand downward, with the elbow bent, in front of the chest with the fingers pointing slightly upwards. Step back with the right foot with the toes pointing directly forward (west). 60R-40L

4. Sink the weight into the right leg and push forward with your left hand, with the elbow slightly bent and palm outward. You are still facing west. 80R-20L

Posture 31　倒攆猴右式

TAO NIEN HOU YU SHIH

TUN

Retreat

Heaven Over Mountain

This posture is the same as posture #29 except the feet always point west. Therefore, there is no toe in on count #3.

Posture 32

倒
攆
猴
左
式

STEP BACK TO DRIVE THE MONKEY AWAY, LEFT STYLE
This posture is the same as posture #30.

SUN
Decrease
Mountain Over Lake

倒
撛
猴
右
式

STEP BACK TO DRIVE THE MONKEY AWAY, RIGHT STYLE

This posture is the same as posture #29 except the feet always point west. Therefore, there is no toe in.

TUN
Retreat
Heaven Over Mountain

Posture 34 斜飛勢

HSIEH FEI SHIH

HUAN

Dispersion

Wind Over Water

During the counts of:

1. Turn your body slightly to the left (to face southwest) and lower your right hand and raise your left hand as if holding a ball. Most of the weight is on the left leg. 0R-100L

2. Turn your body to the right. Bring the arm (right) from beneath the left forearm to the back of the left arm, with the right hand palm up, placed over the left arm near the left elbow. 0R-100L

3. Continue to turn your body to the right and take one big step with your right foot to the far right (northeast) with the heel touching first. Sweep the right arm across to the right with the turn of the body. The palm is in an upward position. Shift the weight to the right leg and turn the left foot slightly inward, pivoting on the heel. 60R-40L

4. Shift 70 percent of your weight to your right foot. The right arm continues to move in a diagonal upward position past and above shoulder level as the body turns to the northeast. At the same time draw back and extend your left hand behind your left thigh in a diagonally downward position, (fingers pointing west). You are now facing northeast. 70R-30L

Posture 35 提手

LIFTING HANDS

During the counts of:

1. As you turn your torso leftward (to face northeast), pick up your left foot and set it down slightly outward (pointing northwest) and shift the weight to it. At the same time turn your palms inward so that they face each other. 0R-100L

2. This count is the same as the respective count of posture #9.

PI

Gracefulness

Mountain Over Fire

SHOULDER-STROKE

This posture is the same as posture #10.

TA CHUANG
Great Strength
Thunder Over Heaven

Posture 37　白亮鶴翅

WHITE CRANE SPREADING WINGS
This posture is the same as posture #11.

TUI
Joyousness
Lake Over lake

左
摟
膝
拗
步

BRUSH LEFT KNEE AND TWIST STEP

This posture is the same as posture #12.

KU
Deterioration
Mountain over Wind

Posture 39 　海底針

HAI TI CHEN

HSIAO KUO

Small Excess

Thunder Over Mountain

During the counts of:

1. Pick up your right foot and set it down with toes turned slightly outward (northwest) and begin to shift the weight to it. Turn the right palm inward. 0R-100L

2. Bring your left hand forward and put your left hand fingers by the crook of your right forearm. At the same time shift your left foot slightly forward and to the right with the toes touching the ground. 100R-0L

3. Gradually lower your body by bending your right knee. 100R-0L

4. Continue to lower your right hand and your body so that your right fingers point directly to the ground below your right knee. You are still facing west. 100R-0L

Posture 40

SHAN T'UNG PEI

TA CH'U
Great Restraint
Mountain Over Heaven

During the counts of:

1. Raise your body and raise your right hand to chest level with the palm facing south and with your left hand still attached to the crook of your right forearm. 100R-0L

2. Continue to raise your right hand and bring it near you right ear with the palm outward and elbow bent. At the same time move your left hand forward with the palm outward and elbow bent. 0R-100L

3. Take a half step forward and leftward with your left foot (with heel touching first) and shift the weight to it. 40R-60L

4. Gradually push upward with your left palm with the elbow slightly bent shifting 70 percent of your weight to the left foot. You are still facing west. 30R-70L

Posture 41

轉身撇身捶

CHUAN SHEN P'IEH SHEN CH'UI

TA KUO

Great Excess

Lake over Wood

During the counts of:

1. Circle your hands clockwise to the right, turning your body in the same direction (north) while shifting your weight to the right foot. At the same time curve your left foot inward facing north. 100R-0L

2. Continue to turn your hands clockwise, downward, leftward and upward until your left hand is near your left temple, with palm outward and elbow bent, and your right is clenched into a fist with knuckles up, in the front of the left side of the body. At the same time shift your weight to the left foot and let the right heel be brought off the ground. 0R-100L

3. Turn your body to the right (east) and raise your right foot to take a half step to the forward right direction with the heel touching first and toes pointing east. Make your right fist circle upward vertically to the right and chop down toward the east, and then withdraw it to the right side of your waist with knuckles down. At the same time gradually shift your weight to your right foot and curve your left toes slightly inward. 60R-40L

4. Shift 70 percent of your weight to your right foot and lastly push upward with your left palm. You are now facing east. 70R-30L

Posture 42

進
步
搬
攔
捶

STEP FORWARD, DEFLECT DOWNWARD, INTERCEPT AND PUNCH

This posture is the same as posture #20 except:

1. Pick up your left foot and set it down (pointing northeast). 100R-0L

LIN

2. Turn body to northeast. 40R-60L

Approaching

3. Toes point southeast (right foot). 0R-100L

Earth Over Lake

Counts 4, 5 and 6 are the same as the respective counts of posture #20.

STEP FORWARD AND WARD-OFF, RIGHT

During the counts of:

1. Shift your weight to your right foot. Turn your body to the left (to face northeast). Open the right fist and let the arm turn with the body to the left. Let your left hand turn with the body also. Raise the left toes and turn the foot slightly outward to the left. At the same time turn your body slightly to the left (to face northeast). 100R-0L

2. Gradually shift your weight to the left foot. 40R-60L

Counts 3 and 4 are the same as the respective counts of posture #4.

CH'IEN

The Creative

Heaven Over Heaven

Posture 44 擖

ROLL-BACK
This posture is the same as posture #5.

K'UN
The Receptive
Earth Over Earth

PRESS

This posture is the same as posture #6.

K'AN
Perilous Water
Water Over Water

Posture 46   按

PUSH
This posture is the same as posture #7.

LI
Adhering Light
Fire Over Fire

單
鞭

SINGLE WHIP

This posture is the same as posture #8.

KO
Revolution
Lake Over Fire

Posture 48

左雲手

TSO YUN SHOU

YI
Increase
Wind Over Thunder

WAVING HANDS IN THE CLOUDS, LEFT

During the counts of:

1. Open your right "hook" hand and turn your right hand, palm down, drawing it back in front near your neck while turning your torso to the right (to face north). Shift your weight to the right foot, turn left foot inward (pointing north), and turn your left hand, palm up, beside your abdomen. Now your hands simulate holding a ball. 100R-0L

2. Keeping the weight on your right foot turn your waist to the left (northeast). Simultaneously circle your left hand upwards and the right hand downwards. Turn the waist back to the front (north). Both hands then face the body. 80R-20L

3. Turn your torso gradually to the left (to face northwest) and shift the weight to the left foot. 30R-70L

4. Continue to turn your torso together with both of your hands to the left. Shift all the weight to the left foot until your right hand, palm up, is near your abdomen and the left hand, palm down, is near your neck. You, again, are simulating the holding of a ball and are facing west. 20R-80L

右雲手

YU YUN SHOU

KUAI

Revolution

Lake Over Heaven

During the counts of:

1. Turn the torso to the right (northwest), lowering the left hand so that the palm faces the body. The right hand rises to neck level with this palm also facing the body. 0R-100L

2. Draw your right foot back in line with your left foot with the toes pointing north (the distance between the feet should be equal to shoulder width). 20R-80L

3. Continue to turn your torso and guide your hands to the right (northeast) and gradually shift your weight to your right foot. 70R-30L

4. Continue to turn your torso and hands to the right until you face east. Your right hand, palm down, is near your neck, and your left hand, palm up is near your abdomen and under your right hand. Again you simulate holding a ball. You are now facing east. 20R-80L

左
雲
手

TSO YUN SHOU

YI

Increase

Wind Over Thunder

During the counts of:

1. Turn the torso to the left (northeast) lowering the right hand so that the palm faces the body. The left hand rises to neck level with the palm also facing the body. 100R-0L.

2. Take a large step to the left side, feet pointing to the front and draw the hands over the right leg. 80R-20L

Counts 3 and 4 are the same as the respective counts of posture #48.

Posture 51

右
雲
手

WAVING HANDS IN THE CLOUDS, RIGHT
This posture is the same as posture #49.

KUAI

Resolution

Lake Over Heaven

WAVING HANDS IN THE CLOUDS, LEFT

This posture is the same as posture #50.

YI

Increase

Wind Over Thunder

Posture 53　　單
　　　　　　　鞭

TAN PIEN

HSU

Waiting

Water Over Heaven

During the counts of:

1. Take a step to the forward right direction (northeast) with your right foot, (heel touching first) and shift the weight to it. Gradually turn your torso to the right. Make a "hook hand" with the fingers pointing down and extend the hand to the northeast. At the same time lower your left hand, palm up, near your abdomen. 100R-0L

2. Gradually turn your torso to the left (northwest) with left heel up and toes pointing west. 100R-0L

3. Continue to turn your torso to the left (west) and step forward and to the left with your left heel touching first. Shift the weight to this leg. Raise your left hand in front of you at the level of your eyes with palm inward and turn your right foot slightly inward. 40R-60L

4. Shift 70 percent of your weight to your left foot. Turn your left palm outward as your eyes, which have accompanied the gradual turn, look across the fingers of your left extended hand. You are now facing west. 30R-70L

Posture 54 高探馬

KAO T'AN MA

LU

The Wanderer

Fire Over Mountain

During the counts of:

1. Pick up your right foot and lower it with the foot turned slightly outward. Shift the weight to it, bending the right knee slightly. 100R-0L

2. Shift your left foot slightly rightward and backward with the heel raised and toes touching the ground. Open your right "hook hand". 100R-0L

3. Turn the left palm upward. The right hand bends so that the fingers touch the left bicep. 100R-0L

4. Draw your left hand backward and extend your right hand forward until your left hand is near your abdomen (with palm up) and your right is in front and over your left hand (with palm downward) with the elbow slightly bent. You still face west. 100R-0L

Posture 55 右分脚

YU FEN CHIO

CHEN
Thunder
Thunder Over Thunder

During the counts of:

1. Sink weight onto right leg. 100R-0L

2. Step with your left foot to the forward left direction and turn the body. Only the heel touches with the toes pointing southwest. 100R-0L

3. Shift your weight to the left foot and gradually separate and circle your hands in opposite directions, upwards and sideways. 40R-60L

4. Continue to circle your hands downward and upward until the wrists join with the right hand outside of the left hand and both palms face inward. At the same time shift your right foot near your left foot with the heel up and toes touching the ground. 0R-100L

5. Turn your palms outward and gradually turn your body to the right (to face northwest). 0R-100L

6. Separate your hands in the opposite directions while at the same time kicking your right foot forward (northwest). Keep your right foot slightly bent with your right hand aligned to your right foot. Your left arm has the elbow bent and fingers pointing upward so as to maintain balance. You are now facing northwest. 0R-100L

Posture 56 左分脚

TSO FEN CHIO

CHIEH
Liberation
Thunder Over Water

During the counts of:

1. Bend the right knee with foot suspended in the air and toes pointing down, and at the same time withdraw the right hand with palm upward. Left hand is palm down. 0R-100L

2. Lower your right foot and step one full step to the northwest with heel touching first; shift the weight to it. At the same time extend the left hand to the southwest with palm down and turn your body slightly to the left (southwest). 60R-40L

3. Circle both hands counterclockwise to the northeast and turn your body slightly to the right (northwest). 80R-20L

4. Join the two hands in a cross shape in front of your upper chest with palms inward and left hand outside of the right hand. Bring the left foot to the right, placing it on the toes which point southwest. 100R-0L

5. Turn the palms outward and turn the body slightly to the left (southwest). 100R-0L

6. Separate your hands in the opposite directions while simultaneously kicking forward with the tip of your left foot. Keep your left foot slightly bent with the instep and your left hand aligned to your left foot. Your right arm has the elbow bent and fingers pointing upward so as to maintain balance. You are now facing southwest. 100R-0L

Posture 57

轉
身
蹬
腳

CHUAN SHEN TENG CHIO

WU WANG

Innocence

Heaven Over Thunder

During the counts of:

1. Withdraw your left hand near your chest and withdraw your left leg with knee bent and foot suspended in the air. At the same time turn your torso slightly to the right (northwest) and extend your hands to the same direction with palms facing one another. 100R-0L

2. Swing your body by turning on your right heel to the left with the toes facing south. Your right hand meets and joins the left hand. The left hand is inside of the right hand, thus forming a cross hands position (body is facing south). 100R-0L

3. Turn your palms outward as you gradually turn your torso to the left (east) and raise your left knee with the sole of the foot held level. 100R-0L

4. Kick forward with the heel of your left foot with toes upward while bringing forward your left hand to the level of your nose. Your right arm is bent at the elbow with fingers of both hands pointing upward so as to maintain balance. You are now facing east. 100R-0L

Posture 58

左
摟
膝
拗
步

BRUSH LEFT KNEE AND TWIST STEP

(Same as posture #12 except as indicated and that you are facing east).

1. Lower left hand near chest and left leg with knee bent. Toes of the left foot are placed on the ground. 100R-0L

2. Turn torso right, circle right hand up by the right ear. Left arm bends slightly turns rightward with body: palm faces body. 100R-0L

3. Same as posture 12, count 3, but facing east.

4. Same as posture 12, count 4, but facing east.

HSIEN

Attraction

Lake Over Mountain

右
摟
膝
拗
步

BRUSH RIGHT KNEE AND TWIST STEP
This posture is the same as posture #15, except you are facing east.

HENG
Duration
Thunder Over Wind

Posture 60   進步栽捶

CHIN PU TSAI CH'UI

P'I
Adversity
Heaven Over Earth

STEP FORWARD AND PUNCH DOWNWARD

During the counts of:

1. Withdraw your weight to the left foot and turn the torso slightly to the right, turning the right foot slightly outward to point southeast. The left palm turns inward. 0R-100L

2. Make a fist with your right hand and hold the "tiger mouth" (space between thumb and forefinger) upward, by your right thigh. The left arm is bent and is chest height with the palm facing the body. Shift your weight to your right foot. 60R-40L

3. Take a step directly forward with your left foot, heel touching first, and shift the weight to it. Brush your left knee with your left hand and hold it beside the thigh (palm backward), and turn your right foot slightly inward (pivoting on the heel). 40R-60L

4. Shift 70 percent of your weight to the left foot and punch downward with your right fist below and near your left knee with the "tiger mouth" facing forward. You are still facing east. 30R-70L

Posture 61　轉身撇身捶

TURN AROUND AND CHOP WITH FIST
During the counts of:
1. Same as Posture #41.

MENG

Youthful Ignorance

Mountain Over Water

2. Same as Posture #41, Count 2, but facing south.
3. Same as Posture #41, Count 3, but facing west.
4. Same as Posture #41, Count 4, but facing west.

進步搬攔捶

STEP FORWARD, DEFLECT DOWNWARD, INTERCEPT AND PUNCH

This posture is the same as posture #20.

YU

Happiness

Thunder Over Earth

右
踢
脚

YU T'I CHIO

CHIEN

Obstruction

Water Over Mountain

KICK UPWARD WITH RIGHT FOOT

During the counts of:

1. Draw your body backward and shift your weight to your right foot. Turn the left toes slightly outward and turn your body slightly to the left (to face southwest). At the same time open your right fist, separate both hands with palms facing outward at ear level. 100R-0L

2. Shift the weight forward to your left foot. At the same time continue to circle your hands downward and inward. As they approach each other along the lower arc of the circle bring them upward and cross them diagonally at the wrists in front of your left foot. Bring the right foot to the front (west) one halfstep with only the toes touching the ground, pointing northwest. 0R-100L

3. Turn the palms outward and turn your body slightly to the right (to face northwest). 0R-100L

4. Kick upward as high as you can comfortably with the tip of your right foot, the sole facing northwest. At the same time bring your right hand to the level of your nose, while your left arm is bent behind and to the left of the left ear. The fingers of both hands point upwards, so as to maintain balance. You are now facing northwest. 0R-100L

Posture 64

左
打
虎

TSO TA HU SHIH

K'UEI

Opposition

Fire Over Lake

During the counts of:

1. Lower your right foot and put it down shoulder width in front and to the right of your left foot. Bring your right hand down, with the palm upward and lower the arm so that it is chest level. The left hand is lowered from its position by the ear so that the arm is parallel to the right arm palm down. Both elbows are bent. You are facing west. (But the feet point southwest.) 0R-100L

2. Shift the weight to the right leg. Continue to bring your hands downward to the side of the waist. You are facing southwest. 100R-0L

3. Gradually turn body to the south and take a big step diagonally in this direction with your left foot (heel touching first) and gradually shift your weight to it. Pivot the right foot slightly inward. At the same time clench both hands into fists and hold them at the same height at chest level, with the "tiger's mouths" facing each other. 40R-60L

4. Turn your waist back to the southeast direction and bring your left hand above the forehead, palm facing out; the right hand is brought to solar plexus level, palm facing down. Sink the entire body. 20R-80L

Posture 65

右打虎

YU TA HU SHIH

KUAN
Contemplation
Wind Over Earth

During the counts of:

1. Turn your body to the right (west) and shift your weight to the right foot and curve your left toes inward as much as you can. Both arms are brought forward, palms up and out from the chest. 100R-0L

2. Continue to lower your arms in front of your lower abdomen. Shift the weight to your left foot. The right foot is brought on to the toe. 0R-100L

3. (The same as posture #64, except where indicated). Step northeast and face northeast. 60R-40L

4. Right fist above, left below. Turn the waist to face northwest. 80R-20L

Posture 66

右
踢
脚

YU T'I CHIO

CHIEN

Obstruction

Water Over Mountain

During the counts of:

1. Turn your body to the left (southwest). Turn the left foot outward by pivoting on the heel and turn your right foot slightly inward. At the same time open the fists and start to circle the hands upward and sideways in opposite directions. The right arm circles rightward and the left, leftward.

Counts 2, 3 and 4 of this posture are the same as #63.

Posture 67

雙
風
貫
耳

SHUANG FENG KUAN ER

SHIH HO

Gnawing

Fire Over Thunder

STRIKE WITH BOTH FISTS

During the counts of:

1. Lower and suspend your right foot with the toes pointing down, bending the knee and keeping the thigh level. 0R-100L

2. Lower your hands and body with palms upward and brush the two sides of your suspended right knee. 0R-100L

3. Step forward and rightward with your right foot (heel touching first, toes pointing northwest) and gradually shift weight to it. Turn your left foot slightly inward. At the same time clench your hands into fists and begin to circle them backward and upward, so that the palms face downward. 60R-40L

4. Shift 70 percent of your weight to the right foot. The elbows are slightly bent (the fists are about shoulder width apart). Sink the body down. You are still facing northwest. 70R-30L

Posture 68

左
踢
脚

TSO T'I CHIO

KUEI MEI
Maiden's Marriage
Thunder Over Lake

KICK UPWARD WITH LEFT FOOT Posture 68

During the counts of:

1. Shift the weight to your left foot and turn your right foot slightly outward. Open the fists and circle the hands to face outwards. 0R-100L

2. Shift the weight to your right foot. Withdraw your left foot and put it beside and slightly in front of your right foot with only the toes touching the ground pointing southwest. Bring your hands inward and cross them at the wrists in front of your chest. The right hand is outside of the left hand and the palms face inward. 100R-0L

3. Turn the palms outward. At the same time turn your body to the left (southwest). 100R-0L

4. Kick upward with your left foot with the sole facing southwest. At the same time bring your left hand forward at the level of your ear; your right arm is bent with the hand behind and by the right ear with fingers of both hands pointing upward so as to maintain balance. You are now facing southwest. 100R-0L

Posture 69

轉
身
蹬
腳

CHUAN SHEN TENG CHIO

PO

Decay

Mountain Over Earth

During the counts of:

1. Lower your left hand sideways to the level of your chest and withdraw your left foot, bending the knee with the foot suspended in the air and toes pointing down. At the same time turn the leg slightly to the left, lower the right hand and bring it toward the left in line with the left arm. Face south. 100R-0L

2. Raise your right heel and turn your body around to the far right by pivoting on the ball of the right foot, until you face south again. Lower your left foot to the ground with the toes pointing south. 40R-60L

3. Circle your hands in opposite directions, as you shift all the weight to the left leg and the right leg is picked up. 0R-100L

4. Continue to circle your hands and cross them in front of your chest, with wrists joined and the right hand placed inside of the left hand (palms facing inward). Pick up the right leg. 0R-100L

5. Turn your palms outward and gradually turn your torso to the right (southwest). 0R-100L

6. Kick forward (west) with your right sole, with toes upward, while you chop forward with your right hand at the level of your nose. Your left arm is bent back behind your left ear with the fingers pointing upward so as to maintain balance. Now you are facing west. 0R-100L

Posture 70

撇
身
捶

CHOP WITH FIST

During the counts of:

    1. Draw back and suspend your right foot with the knee bent and toes pointing down. Circle your right hand clockwise, downward and leftward, with the palm inward; lower your left hand with the palm outward. 0R-100L

    2. Same as Posture #19, Count 2.

TING

The Cauldron

Fire Over Wood

進
步
搬
攔
捶

STEP FORWARD, DEFLECT DOWNWARD, INTERCEPT AND PUNCH

During the counts of:

1. Pick up your left foot and set it down turned slightly outward in the southwest direction.

Counts 2 to 6 are the same as the respective counts of posture #20.

YU

Happiness

Thunder Over Earth

Posture 72 如封似閉

WITHDRAW AND PUSH
This posture is the same as posture #21.

CHIA JEN
The Family
Wind Over Fire

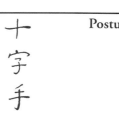

CROSSING HANDS

This posture is the same as posture #22.

MING YI
Darkened Light
Earth Over Fire

Posture 74

抱
虎
歸
山

EMBRACE THE TIGER AND RETURN TO THE MOUNTAIN
This posture is the same as posture #23.

KEN
Resting
Mountain Over Mountain

擝

ROLL-BACK

This posture is the same as posture #5.

K'UN
The Receptive
Earth Over Earth

Posture 76 擠

PRESS

This posture is the same as posture #6.

K'AN

Perilous Water

Water Over Water

按

PUSH

This posture is the same as posture #7.

LI
Adhering Light
Fire Over Fire

Posture 78　横單鞭

HENG TAN PIEN

PI

Union

Water Over Earth

During the counts of:

1. Shift your weight gradually to your left foot; your palms face downward; your hands are parallel with your shoulders. 20R-80L

2. Turn your torso to the left until it faces northeast. At the same time pivot on your right heel, carrying the toes slightly inward. 0R-100L

3. As you shift your weight back to your right leg, allow the body to turn to the right so that you face southeast. As you bend your right elbow to withdraw your right hand southward, allow the fingers to point down and lightly close together at the tips (as if holding a drop of water) thus forming a hook near the right armpit. Bring the left hand to rest, palm up, by the abdomen. 80R-20L

4. Pivot on the ball of the left foot, so that the toes point northeast with the rising heel turning rightward. Extend the "hook hand" rightward so that the knuckles face southeast. The trunk turns northeast. 100R-0L

5. As your trunk continues to turn leftward, step to the front left (north) with your left foot, heel down first and then toes (to point north). The left heel should not be directly in front of your right heel. The feet should be in a shoulder width position. Gradually shift your weight to your left foot (bending the left knee) and allow your waist to turn leftward so that you face north; the left hand with the palm inward, is carried leftward until it is opposite the left breast and at the same time raise your right foot slightly and turn it slightly inward by pivoting on the heel. 40R-60L

6. Sink your weight to the left foot until 70 percent of your weight has been shifted to it. Turn your left palm outward with the arm slightly bent, as your eyes, which have accompanied the gradual turn, look past the finger tips. You are now facing north. 30R-70L

Posture 79

野
馬
分
鬃
右
式

YEH MA FEN TSUNG YU SHIH

LU

The Wanderer

Fire Over Mountain

During the counts of:

1. Shift your weight to the right foot and turn your left foot inward about 20 degrees. 100R-0L

2. Shift your weight to the left foot. Turn your body to the right (to face northeast). At the same time bring your left hand over toward the front of the chest, with the palm down and elbow bent. Open your right "hook hand" and lower it near your left waist with the palm up, you simulate holding a ball in your hands. 0R-100L

3. Take a half-step forward with your right foot toward the southeast (heel touching first) and shift the weight to it. Turn the left foot slightly inward. Continue to turn your body to the right (east). Bring the right forearm forward toward the east, palm up. During this move your left hand moves downward, palm facing back. 60R-40L

4. Shift 70 percent of your weight to the right foot and continue to raise your right forearm upwards and out until your right hand is at the height of your nose with palm facing slanting upward over your right leg and fingers pointing southeast. You are now facing southeast. 70R-30L

Posture 80   野馬分鬃左式

YEH MA FEN TSUNG TSO SHIH

TS'UI
Gathering
Lake Over Earth

During the counts of:

1. Shift your weight to the left foot and turn the right foot inwards about 20 degrees. 0R-100L

2. Shift your weight to the right foot and lower your right hand to the level of your chest with palm down, elbow bent, and move your left hand near the right side of your waist with the palm upward. You simulate holding a ball in your hands. Turn your body gradually to the left (to face east). 100R-0L

3. Take a half-step forward (northeast) with your left foot, heel touching first, and shift the weight to it; curve the right foot slightly inward. At the same time gradually begin to bring your left forearm forward with palm up and move your right hand downward. 40R-60L

4. Shift 70 percent of your weight to the left foot. Continue to raise your left forearm upward and out (toward the northeast) and until it is at the height of your nose with the palm facing upward at an angle over your left leg. The fingers of the left hand point northeast. You are now facing northeast. 30R-70L

Posture 81　　野馬分鬃右式

YEH MA FEN TSUNG YU SHIH

LU

The Wanderer

Fire Over Mountain

During the counts of:

1. Sink your weight to your right foot and turn your left foot slightly outward. 100R-0L

Counts 2, 3 and 4 are the same as in Posture # 79.

Posture 82

左
掤

WARD-OFF, LEFT

During the counts of:

1. Sink weight onto left foot, turn right foot slightly inward. 0R-100L

CH'IEN

The Creative

Heaven Over

Heaven

2. Shift weight to right foot, turn body slightly to left (face east). Withdraw and lower right hand near chest, palm down, move left hand near right side of waist, palm up. Turn body slightly left (east). 100R-0L

3. This is the same as Posture #3, Count 5.

4. Sink 70 percent of weight to left foot, face north. 30R-70L

WARD-OFF, RIGHT

This posture is the same as posture #4.

CH'IEN
The Creative
Heaven Over
Heaven

Posture 84

ROLL-BACK
This posture is the same as posture #5.

K'UN
The Receptive
Earth Over Earth

擠

PRESS

This posture is the same as posture #6.

K'AN
Perilous Water
Water Over Water

Posture 86   按

PUSH
This posture is the same as posture #7.

LI
Adhering Light
Fire Over Fire

SINGLE WHIP
This posture is the same as posture #8.

KO
Revolution
Lake Over Fire

Posture 88

玉
女
穿
梭

YU NU CH'UAN SHO

SUNG
Conflict
Heaven Over Water

During the counts of:

1. Shift your weight to the right foot. Gradually turn your body to the right (to face northeast) and pivoting on the left heel, turn the left foot inward so that the toes point north. At the same time bring your left hand to point northeast with the palm facing inward and on line with the right elbow. 100R-0L

2. Shift your weight to the left foot so that the right foot is brought onto its toes (pointing northeast). Left arm bends so fingers point upwards; left is palm up with fingers touching the inner side of the right elbow. 0R-100L

3. Bring your right foot slightly out to the forward right direction with the heel touching first and toes pointing southeast, then set it down. Turn your body to the right (to face east) and gradually shift the weight to the right foot. At the same time your left hand turns palm upward, and both hands are on line with each other. 60R-40L

4. Take a step with your left foot forward to the northeast, heel touching first, continue to circle your right hand upward and forward, stop it near your right ear with palm forward and elbow bent. Left arm forms a bow and the palm faces the body. 100R-0L

5. Continue to raise your left hand upward until it is over your left forehead and turn the palm outward. The right hand moves, palm outward, to the front of the body. At the same time gradually turn your body to the left (to face northeast), and begin to shift your weight to the left foot; turn your right foot slightly inward. 40R-60L

6. Shift 70 percent of your weight to the left foot and push your right hand upwards (with the energy of the whole body) with the right elbow slightly bent, with the palm facing outward. You are now facing northeast. 30R-70L

Posture 89

玉
女
穿
梭

YU NU CH'UAN SHO

LU
Treading
Heaven Over Lake

During the counts of:

1. Shift your weight to your right foot and slowly turn your body to the right (to face south) while pivoting on the left heel. Turn the left foot inward as far as possible so that the toes point south. At the same time bring your right hand to point south, with the palm on line and facing the left elbow. 100R-0L

2. Shift your weight back to the left foot so that the right foot is brought to its toes pointing southwest. At the same time bring your left hand so that the fingers point up and the right hand fingers touch the inner side of the left elbow, palm up. 0R-100L

3. Bring your left foot slightly to the east, heel touching first. Shift your weight onto it. Both arms are brought on line with each other, palms up. The right hand is brought directly out from the left elbow. 0R-100L

4. Take a step northwest with your right foot with the heel touching first and toes pointing northwest. At the same time continue to circle your left hand upward and forward to stop near your left ear with the elbow bent and palm forward. The right arm forms a bow and the palm faces the body. 0R-100L

5. Gradually shift your weight to the right foot and continue to turn your body to the right (to face northwest). At the same time raise your right hand over your forehead with the palm forward and elbow bent. Turn your left foot slightly inward. The left hand moves to the front of the body. 60R-40L

6. Shift 70 percent of your weight to the right foot and push upward with your left hand together with the energy of your whole body as one unit. You are now facing northwest. 70R-30L

Posture 90

玉
女
穿
梭

YU NU CH'UAN SHO

SUN
Penetrating Wind
Wind Over Wind

During the counts of:

1. Sink your weight to the right foot, and lower both hands to chest level. 100R-0L

2. Sink into your left foot, bring the right arm up and left palm to right elbow, as before. 0R-100L

3. Shift your weight to the right foot. At the same time begin to circle your right hand counterclockwise, downward and backward, and gradually raise your left hand upward and to the left with the palm facing you. 60R-40L

4. Step with your left foot forward and leftward (southwest) with the heel touching first. Continue to circle your right hand upward and forward and stop it beside your right ear with the palm forward. Left arm forms a bow and plam faces the body. 100R-0L

5. Begin to shift your weight to your left foot and gradually turn your body to the left (to face southwest). At the same time continue to raise your left hand upward and over your forehead, turning the palm outward with the elbow slightly bent. Turn your right foot slightly inward. The right hand continues to circle, palm down, to the front of the body. 40R-60L

6. Sink 70 percent of your weight to the left foot and push upward with your right hand together with the energy of your whole body as one unit. Now you are facing southwest. 30R-70L

Posture 91

玉女穿梭

YU NU CH'UAN SHO

K'UN

Oppression

Lake Over Water

During the counts of:

1. Shift your weight to the right foot, and gradually turn your body to the right (to face north) while pivoting on the left heel turning the left foot inward so that it points north. Bring the arms around in the usual fashion. 100R-0L

2. Shift your weight to the left foot so that your right foot is raised to its toes pointing north.Bring the arms and hands into the usual position. 0R-100L

3. The same as #3 of Posture #84 only the direction is west. 0R-100L

4. Step with your right foot forward and rightward, with the heel touching first so that the toes finish pointing southeast. At the same time continue to circle your left hand upward and forward and stop it near your left ear with the palm forward and continue to raise your right hand to head level. 0R-100L

5. Gradually shift your weight to the right foot and continue to turn your body to the right (to face southeast). At the same time raise your right hand over your forehead and turn your palm outward with the elbow slightly bent. Turn your left foot slightly inward. The left hand circles forward to the front of the body, palm down. 60R-40L

6. Shift 70 percent of your weight to the right foot and push upward with your left hand together with the energy of your whole body as one unit. Now you are facing southeast. 70R-30L

Posture 92　左掤

WARD-OFF, LEFT
This posture is the same as posture #82.

CH'IEN
The Creative
Heaven Over
Heaven

右
掤

WARD-OFF, RIGHT

This posture is the same as posture #4.

CH'IEN
The Creative
Heaven Over Heaven

Posture 94 擴

ROLL-BACK

This posture is the same as posture #5.

K'UN

The Receptive

Earth Over Earth

PRESS

This posture is the same as posture #6.

K'AN
Perilous Water
Water Over Water

Posture 96 按

PUSH
This posture is the same as posture #7.

LI
Adhering Light
Fire Over Fire

SINGLE WHIP

This posture is the same as posture #8.

KO
Revolution
Lake Over Fire

Posture 98　左雲手

WAVING HANDS IN THE CLOUDS, LEFT
This posture is the same as posture #48.

YI
Increase
Wind Over Thunder

WAVING HANDS IN THE CLOUDS, RIGHT

This posture is the same as posture #49.

KUAI

Resolution

Lake Over Heaven

Posture 100

左雲手

WAVING HANDS IN THE CLOUDS, LEFT
This posture is the same as posture #50.

YI
Increase
Wind Over Thunder

右雲手

WAVING HANDS IN THE CLOUDS, RIGHT
This posture is the same as posture #49.

KUAI
Resolution
Lake Over Heaven

Posture 102

左云手

WAVING HANDS IN THE CLOUDS, LEFT
This posture is the same as posture #50.

YI

Increase

Wind Over Thunder

單
鞭

SINGLE WHIP

This posture is the same as posture #53.

HSU

Waiting

Water Over Heaven

Posture 104 單鞭下勢

TAN PIEN HSIA SHIH

FU
Returning
Earth Over Thunder

SINGLE WHIP SQUATTING DOWN   **Posture 104**

During the counts of:

1. Step back with your right foot with the toes pointing north. Draw back and shift all your weight to your right leg and bend the knee. 100R-0L

2. Turn the waist to face north, turning the left foot in slightly. The left hand moves down to waist level, palm down. Right "hook hand" remains. 80R-20L

3. Turn your left foot, pivoting on the heel, so that the toes point west. At the same time lower your left hand so that it traces an arc down along the left thigh and forward with the palm facing north. Shift the weight of the left leg and turn in the right foot. 60R-40L

4. Slowly rise, straightening the right knee. Your right hand is still kept hooked behind you (toward the northeast) to maintain balance and your left hand continues forward with the palm facing north. You are now facing west. 30R-70L

Posture 105

金鷄獨立右式

CHIN CHI TU LI YU SHIH

HSIAO CH'U
Minor Restraint
Wind Over Heaven

During the counts of:

1. Shift the weight to the right leg and turn the left foot out (southwest). Shift your weight entirely to your left leg and keeping it slightly bent, lower your left hand beside your left thigh with the palm facing inward. At the same time open your right "hook hand" and lower it beside your right thigh with the palm inward. 0R-100L

2. Raise your right hand forward and up to head level with the elbow bent, fingers pointing up and the palm facing south. At the same time lift your right foot forward and upward with the knee bent and toes pointing down so that your right elbow is above your right knee, forming a perpendicular line from knee to hand. You are still facing west. 0R-100L

Posture 106

金
鷄
獨
立 左
式

CHIN CHI TU LI TSO SHIH

SHENG

Ascending

Earth Over Wood

During the counts of:

1. Take a half step backward with your right foot, setting it down turned slightly outward, and shift the weight to it with the knee slightly bent. At the same time lower your right hand and put it beside your right thigh with the palm upward. 100R-0L

2. Raise your left hand forward up to head level with the elbow bent, fingers pointing up and palm facing north. At the same time lift up your left foot with the toes pointing down and knee bent, so that your left elbow is above your left knee forming a perpendicular line. You are still facing west. 100R-0L

Posture 107　右倒撞猴

STEP BACK TO DRIVE THE MONKEY AWAY, RIGHT STYLE

During the counts of:

TUN
Retreat
Heaven Over
Mountain

1. Lower left foot in front of right foot with only toes touching ground. Turn body right (face north) At the same time extend left arm forward at shoulder height, palm down, circle right hand counterclockwise, backward and upward to shoulder height, palm up. Face north.

Counts 2, 3 and 4 are the same as the respective counts of posture #29.

左倒撵猴

STEP BACK TO DRIVE THE MONKEY AWAY, LEFT STYLE
This posture is the same as posture #30.

SUN
Decrease
Mountain Over Lake

Posture 109

右倒攆猴

STEP BACK TO DRIVE THE MONKEY AWAY, RIGHT STYLE
This posture is the same as posture #31.

TUN
Retreat
Heaven Over
Mountain

左
倒
攆
猴

STEP BACK TO DRIVE THE MONKEY AWAY, LEFT STYLE

This posture is the same as posture #32.

SUN
Decrease
Mountain Over Lake

Posture 111

右
倒
撵
猴

STEP BACK TO DRIVE THE MONKEY AWAY, RIGHT STYLE
This posture is the same as posture #33.

TUN

Retreat

Heaven Over

Mountain

斜
飛
式

DIAGONAL FLYING POSTURE

This posture is the same as posture #34.

HUAN
Dispersion
Wind Over Water

Posture 113 提手

LIFTING HANDS
This posture is the same as posture #35.

PI
Gracefulness
Mountain Over Fire

SHOULDER-STROKE

This posture is the same as posture #10.

TA CHUANG
Great Strength
Thunder Over
Heaven

Posture 115

白鶴亮翅

WHITE CRANE SPREADING WINGS
This posture is the same as posture #11.

TUI

Joyousness

Lake Over Lake

左
摟
膝
拗
步

BRUSH LEFT KNEE AND TWIST STEP

This posture is the same as posture #12.

KU
Deterioration
Mountain Over
Wind

Posture 117　海底針

NEEDLE AT SEA BOTTOM
This posture is the same as posture #39.

HSIAO KUO
Small Excess
Thunder Over
Mountain

扇
通
背

FAN PENETRATES THE BACK

This posture is the same as posture #40.

TA CH'U
Great Restraint
Mountain Over
Heaven

Posture 119

轉
身
白
蛇
吐
信

TURN AROUND AND WHITE SNAKE PUTS OUT TONGUE

This posture is the same as Posture # 41, except on count #3 the palm
is opened (palm up) and remains open during count #4.

CHUN

Initial Hardship

Water Over

Thunder

進
步
搬
攔
捶

STEP FORWARD, DEFLECT DOWNWARD, INTERCEPT AND PUNCH

This posture is the same as posture #42.

LIN
Approaching
Earth Over Lake

Posture 121

上
步
掤

STEP FORWARD AND WARD-OFF RIGHT
This posture is the same as posture #43.

CH'IEN
The Creative
Heaven Over
Heaven

ROLL-BACK

This posture is the same as posture #5.

K'UN
The Receptive
Earth Over Earth

Posture 123 擠

PRESS
This posture is the same as posture #6.

K'AN
Perilous Water
Water Over Water

按

PUSH

This posture is the same as posture #7.

LI
Adhering Light
Fire Over Fire

Posture 125　罩鞭

SINGLE WHIP
This posture is the same as posture #8.

KO
Revolution
Lake Over Fire

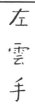

WAVING HANDS IN THE CLOUDS, LEFT

This posture is the same as posture #48.

YI
Increase
Wind Over Thunder

Posture 127 右雲手

WAVING HANDS IN THE CLOUDS, RIGHT
This posture is the same as posture #49.

KUAI
Resolution
Lake Over Heaven

WAVING HANDS IN THE CLOUDS, LEFT

This posture is the same as posture #50.

YI
Increase
Wind Over Thunder

Posture 129　右雲手

WAVING HANDS IN THE CLOUDS, RIGHT
This posture is the same as posture #49.

KUAI
Resolution
Lake Over Heaven

左
雲
手

WAVING HANDS IN THE CLOUDS, LEFT

This posture is the same as posture #50.

YI

Increase

Wind Over Thunder

Posture 131

SINGLE WHIP
This posture is the same as posture #53.

HSU

Waiting

Water Over Heaven

高
探
馬

HIGH PAT ON HORSE

This posture is the same as posture #54.

LU

The Wanderer

Fire Over Mountain

Posture 133 穿掌

CH'UAN CHANG

SHIH
Military Forces
Earth Over Water

During the counts of:

1. Lower your body and bend your right knee slightly. 100R-0L

2. Take half a step with your left foot to the forward left direction with the heel touching first. Withdraw your right hand, palm down and elbow bent. 100R-0L

3. Bring your left hand palm up forward past the back of your right hand. Gradually shift your weight to your left foot. 40R-60L

4. Shift 70 percent of your weight to the left foot. Continue to withdraw your right hand and to bring your left hand forward until your right hand is under the left arm, near your left armpit, (with the palm down) and your left hand is in front at neck level with the palm upward and elbow slightly bent. You are still facing west. 30R-70L

Posture 134

轉
身
十
字
腿

CHUAN SHEN TENG CHIO

SUNG

Conflict

Heaven Over Water

During the counts of:

1. Bending the left arm and extending slightly the right arm, withdraw your left hand (palm up) on the back of your right hand (palm down) while you shift your weight to the right foot and gradually turn your body to the right (to face northeast). At the same time turn the left foot inward to point north. 100R-0L

2. Shift the weight to the left foot and let the right foot be brought onto the toes. Slide the hand underneath the right wrist, so that both palms face down. 0R-100L

3. Turn the body to face east. Bring both hands, palms facing outwards and crossed (left hand in front of right), to chest and neck level. Simultaneously raise the right leg to the level. 0R-100L

4. Kick forward with your right sole with the toes upward while you separate the left hand outward to the north and the right hand to the south. Both hands are nose level with the elbows well bent. Now you are facing east. 0R-100L

Posture 135

摟膝指襠捶

LOU HSI CHI TANG CH'UI

CH'IEN
Humility
Earth Over Mountain

This Posture is the same as Posture # 60, except for count # 4.

4. Shift 70 percent of your weight to your left foot and strike out with your right fist toward your opponent's groin with the fist slightly downward and "tigermouth" upward. You are still facing east. 30R-70L

Posture 136 上步掤

STEP FORWARD AND WARD-OFF, RIGHT
This posture is the same as posture #43.

KUAI

Resolution

Lake Over Heaven

ROLL-BACK

This posture is the same as posture #5.

K'UN
The Receptive
Earth Over Earth

Posture 138

PRESS
This posture is the same as posture #6.

K'AN
Perilous Water
Water Over Water

按

PUSH

This posture is the same as posture #7.

LI
Adhering Light
Fire Over Fire

Posture 140　單鞭

SINGLE WHIP
This posture is the same as posture #8.

KO
Revolution
Lake Over Fire

單
鞭
下
勢

SINGLE WHIP SQUATTING DOWN

This posture is the same as posture #104.

FU
Returning
Earth Over Thunder

Posture 142　上步七星

SHANG PU CH'I HSING

FENG
Abundance
Thunder Over Fire

During the counts of:

1. Shift your entire weight to your right foot; toe out the left foot and then shift all the weight back onto the left foot. Both hands circle up to chest level, palms down. 0R-100L

2. Take one-half step forward with your right foot with only the toes touching the ground, in front of the left foot. Carry both hands to the front of your chest, clenching both hands into fists. Join them at the wrists with the left hand inside of the right hand and "tiger mouths" facing you. You are still facing west. 0R-100L

Posture 143 退步跨虎

T'UI PU K'UA HU

KOU
Encountering
Heaven Over Wind

During the counts of:

1. Draw back your right foot one step; set it down with the toes
pointing northwest and shift the weight to it. At the same time turn your
body slightly to the right, open your fists and bring both hands downward and backward. 100R-0L

2. Turn your body slightly to the left (to face west). Circle your right
hand backward and upward and hold it beside your right ear, with the
fingers up, forearm vertical and palm forward. At the same time continue to lower your left hand and hold it beside your left hip joint with the
palm backward. Shift your left foot slightly rightward, with only the toes
touching the ground and the heel in line with your right heel. You are
still facing west. 100R-0L

Posture 144

轉
身
擺
蓮

CHUAN SHEN PAI LIEN

WEI CHI
Before Completion
Fire Over Water

During the counts of:

1. Turn your body slightly to the left (to face southwest), raise your left hand and lower your right hand extending them both to the southwest at chest height, so that they are parallel with the palms facing each other. At the same time shift your left foot slightly to the left with the toes pointing southwest and slightly off the ground. 100R-0L

2. Turn your palms downward and with the ball of your right foot on the ground, make a spinning turn to the right, (to face south). Place your left foot down (on the toes) in front of your right foot with the left foot pointing southeast. The hands are parallel at shoulder height with the fingers pointing south. 20R-80L

3. Continue to turn your body to the right until you face west with the right toes facing north and hands parallel at chest height with the palms down. Gradually shift your weight to your left foot as the toes turn southwest. 0R-100L

4. Continue to turn your body to the right (northwest) and shift your weight entirely to the left foot. At the same time pick up the right toes and circle your right foot slightly to the right and then place the toes on the ground pointing west. 0R-100L

5. Raise your right foot with the toes upward and circle the foot clockwise (leftward, upward and rightward) with the toes brushing your left palm. 0R-100L

6. Continue to circle your right foot rightward at hip joint level to the right palm with toes upward until the sole faces west. Now you are facing west. 0R-100L

Posture 145

彎
弓
射
虎

WAN KUNG SHE HU

CHING

The Well

Water Over Wood

During the counts of:

1. Lower both hands to chest level with the palms facing down. Lower your right leg near your left leg with the knee slightly bent, toes pointing down and foot slightly off the ground. 0R-100L

2. Step diagonally forward to the right (the heel touching first) with your right foot (northwest). Make both palms into a fist and hold at a level. Turn the left foot in. 60R-40L

3. Gradually shift your weight to your left foot, turn your body to the left (to face west). At the same time clench your hands so that your right fist is near your right ear with the knuckles inward and elbow bent, and your left fist is dropped down in front of your throat with the knuckles upward. 60R-40L

4. Extend your left fist forward to the southwest. The elbow is slightly bent with the "tiger-mouths" of both fists facing each other. You are now facing west. 70R-30L

Posture 146 搬身捶

TURN BODY AND CHOP

During the counts of:

1. Raise left foot, set down on heel, foot turned outward. 0R-100L

TING

The Cauldron

Fire Over Wind

2. Shift weight to left foot, open fists, lower hands near left side, palms downward. 0R-100L

3. Step right (northwest), heel touching first. Turn left foot slightly inward. Turn body to right, clench right hand into a fist. 60R-40L

4. Circle right fist northwest diagonally upward. Extend left hand back, waist level, palm down. You are now facing northwest. 70R-30L

進
步
搬
攔
捶

STEP FORWARD, DEFLECT DOWNWARD, INTERCEPT AND PUNCH

During the counts of:

1. Pick up your left foot and set it down with the foot turned slightly outward (southwest).

Counts 2 to 6 are the same as the respective counts of posture #20.
0R-100L

YU

Happiness

Thunder Over Earth

Posture 148

如封似閉

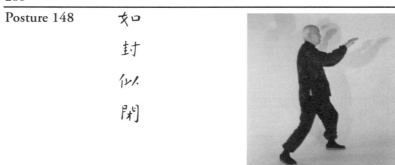

WITHDRAW AND PUSH
This posture is the same as posture #21.

CHIA JEN
The Family
Wind Over Fire

十字手

CROSSING HANDS

This posture is the same as posture #22.

MING YI
Darkened Light
Earth Over Fire

Posture 150

合太極

HO T'AI-CHI

CHI CHI
After Completion
Water Over Fire

During the counts of:

1. Gradually raise your body and begin to lower your hands with the palms down. Shift the weight equally to both legs.

2. Lower your hands near your waist, with palms turning in to face the body, left hand on the outside, right hand on the inside.

3. Separate your hands and bring them beside the thighs, with the fingers down.

4. Bend your elbows slightly with the palms backward. The center of gravity is between the two feet. You are now facing north.

APPENDIX A

THE 150 POSTURE SOLO FORM REFERENCE GUIDE
Arranged by Master T. T. Liang

Body Direction Upon Completion	Rhythm	Posture
N.	2	1. Preparation
N.	6	2. Beginning
N.	6	3. Ward-Off, Left
E.	4	4. Ward-Off, Right
NE	4	5. Roll-Back
E.	4	6. Press
E.	4	7. Push
W.	6	8. Single Whip
N.	2	9. Lifting Hands
N.	2	10. Shoulder-Stroke
W.	2	11. White Crane Spreading Wings
W.	4	12. Brush Left Knee and Twist Step
W.	2	13. Playing the Guitar
W.	4	14. Brush Left Knee and Twist Step
W.	4	15. Brush Right Knee and Twist Step
W.	4	16. Brush Left Knee and Twist Step
W.	2	17. Playing the Guitar
W.	4	18. Brush Left Knee and Twist Step
NW	2	19. Chop with Fist
W.	6	20. Step Forward, Deflect Downward, Intercept and Punch
W.	4	21. Withdraw and Push
N.	4	22. Crossing Hands
SW	4	23. Embrace the Tiger and Return to the Mountain
E.	4	24. Roll-Back
SE.	4	25. Press
SE	4	26. Push
NW	6	27. Slanting Single Whip
W.	6	28. Punch Under Elbow
W.	4	29. Step Back to Drive the Monkey Away, Right Style
W.	4	30. Step Back to Drive the Monkey Away, Left Style
W.	4	31. Step Back to Drive the Monkey Away, Right Style
W.	4	32. Step Back to Drive the Monkey Away, Left Style
W.	4	33. Step Back to Drive the Monkey Away, Right Style

NE	4	34. Diagonal Flying Posture
N.	2	35. Lifting Hands
N.	2	36. Shoulder-Stroke
W.	2	37. White Crane Spreading Wings
W.	4	38. Brush Left Knee and Twist Step
W.	4	39. Needle At Sea Bottom
W.	4	40. Fan Penetrates the Back
E.	4	41. Turn Around and Chop
E.	6	42. Step Forward, Deflect Downward, Intercept and Punch
E.	4	43. Step Forward and Ward-Off, Right
NE	4	44. Roll-Back
E.	4	45. Press
E.	4	46. Push
W.	6	47. Single Whip
W.	4	48. Waving Hands in the Clouds, Left
E.	4	49. Waving Hands in the Clouds, Right
W.	4	50. Waving Hands in the Clouds, Left
E.	4	51. Waving Hands in the Clouds, Right
W.	4	52. Waving Hands in the Clouds, Left
W.	4	53. Single Whip
W.	4	54. High Pat on Horse
NW.	6	55. Separating Right Foot
SW	6	56. Separating Left Foot
E.	4	57. Turn Around and Strike with Heel
E.	4	58. Brush Left Knee and Twist Step
E.	4	59. Brush Right Knee and Twist Step
E.	4	60. Step Forward and Punch Downward
W.	4	61. Turn Around and Chop with Fist
W.	6	62. Step Forward, Deflect Downward, Intercept and Punch
NW	4	63. Kick Upward with Right Foot
SW	4	64. Strike Tiger, Left Style
NW.	4	65. Strike Tiger, Right Style
NW.	4	66. Kick Upward with Right Foot
NW.	4	67. Strike with Both Fists
SW	4	68. Kick Upward with Left Foot
W.	6	69. Turn Around and Kick with Heel (Right Foot)
NW	2	70. Chop with Fist
W.	6	71. Step Forward, Deflect Downward, Intercept and Punch
W.	4	72. Withdraw and Push
N.	4	73. Crossing Hands
SE	4	74. Embrace the Tiger and Return to the Mountain
E.	4	75. Roll-Back

SE	4	76. Press
SE	4	77. Push
N.	6	78. Horizontal Single Whip
SE	4	79. Parting Wild Horse's Mane, Right Style
NE	4	80. Parting Wild Horse's Mane, Left Style
SE	4	81. Parting Wild Horse's Mane, Right Style
N.	4	82. Ward-Off, Left
E.	4	83. Ward-Off, Right
NE	4	84. Roll-Back
E.	4	85. Press
E.	4	86. Push
W.	6	87. Single Whip
NE.	6	88. Fair Lady Weaving at Shuttle (l)
NW.	6	89. Fair Lady Weaving at Shuttle (2)
SW.	6	90. Fair Lady Weaving at Shuttle (3)
SE.	6	91. Fair Lady Weaving at Shuttle (4)
N.	4	92. Ward-Off, Left
E.	4	93. Ward-Off, Right
NE.	4	94. Roll-Back
E.	4	95. Press
E.	4	96. Push
W.	6	97. Single Whip
W.	4	98. Waving Hands in the Clouds, Left
E.	4	99. Waving Hands in the Clouds, Right
W.	4	100. Waving Hands in the Clouds, Left
E.	4	101. Waving Hands in the Clouds, Right
W.	4	102. Waving Hands in the Clouds, Left
W.	4	103. Single Whip
W.	4	104. Single Whip Squatting Down
W.	2	105. Golden Rooster Standing on One Leg, Right Style
W.	2	106. Golden Rooster Standing on One Leg, Left Style
W.	4	107. Step Back to Drive the Monkey Away, Right Style
W.	4	108. Step Back to Drive the Monkey Away, Left Style
W.	4	109. Step Back to Drive the Monkey Away, Right Style
W.	4	110. Step Back to Drive the Monkey Away, Left Style
W.	4	111. Step Back to Drive the Monkey Away, Right Style

NE.	4	112. Diagonal Flying Posture
N.	2	113. Lifting Hands
N.	2	114. Shoulder-Stroke
W.	2	115. White Crane Spreading Wings
W.	4	116. Brush Left Knee and Twist Step
W.	4	117. Needle at Sea Bottom
W.	4	118. Fan Penetrates the Back
E.	4	119. Turn Around and White Snake Puts out Tongue
E.	6	120. Step Forward, Deflect Downward, Intercept and Punch
E.	4	121. Step Forward and Ward-Off, Right
NE.	4	122. Roll-Back
E.	4	123. Press
E.	4	124. Push
W.	6	125. Single Whip
W.	4	126. Waving Hands in the Clouds, Left
E.	4	127. Waving Hands in the Clouds, Right
W.	4	128. Waving Hands in the Clouds, Left
E.	4	129. Waving Hands in the Clouds, Right
W.	4	130. Waving Hands in the Clouds, Left
W.	4	131. Single Whip
W.	4	132. High Pat on Horse
W.	4	133. Thrusting Hand
E.	4	134. Turn Around and Kick with Heel (Right Foot)
E.	4	135. Brush Knee and Punch Groin
E.	4	136. Step Forward and Ward-Off, Right
NE.	4	137. Roll-Back
E.	4	138. Press
E.	4	139. Push
W.	6	140. Single Whip
W.	4	141. Single Whip Squatting Down
W.	2	142. Step Forward to the Seven Star
W.	2	143. Step Back to Ride the Tiger
W.	6	144. Turn Around and Sweep with Leg (Right Foot)
SW.	4	145. Bend the Bow and Shoot Tiger
NW.	4	146. Turn Body and Chop
W.	6	147. Step Forward, Deflect Downward, Intercept and Punch
W.	4	148. Withdraw and Push
N.	4	149. Crossing Hands
N.	4	150. Conclusion of T'ai-Chi

Comment Card

DRAGON DOOR PUBLICATIONS
Books to Enhance Your Life

Phone: (612) 645-0517
Fax: (612) 644-5676

At **DRAGON DOOR** we believe that the two most important people in the publishing process are the author and the reader. If you have a comment for the author of this book, would like a catalog of our other titles, or you are interested in information about workshops/classes on T'ai Chi and related Chinese internal arts, please use this card.

Send Catalog ☐   Send Workshop Information ☐

Book Title (please print) _____

Comments _____

_____

_____

Name_____

Address _____

City, State, Zip _____

Dragon Door Publications, Inc.
P. O. Box 4381
St. Paul, MN 55104

About the Compiler

Stuart Alve Olson began learning the Chinese language during his residency at the City of Ten-Thousand Buddhas in Ukiah, CA (1979-1980). In 1982 he was invited to live in Master Liang's home in St. Cloud, Minnesota (the only student granted this honor). Staying with Master Liang for five years, Stuart studied both T'ai Chi Ch'uan and Chinese language under his tutelage. Since that time he has travelled extensively throughout the United States with Master Liang assisting him in teaching T'ai Chi Ch'uan. Stuart has also taught in Canada, Indonesia and travelled throughout Asia. He lives in Minneapolis, Minnesota where he both teaches T'ai Chi Ch'uan and compiles and translates various Chinese philosophical, martial arts and health oriented books for Dragon Door Publications.

For further information
or a catalog of titles, write to:

Dragon Door Publications
P.O. Box 4381
St. Paul MN 55104

Cultivating the Ch'i

Chen Kung Series, Volume One

Translated by Stuart Alve Olson
$12.95, paper, 164 pages,
5-1/2" x 8-1/2",
101 illustrations.
ISBN O-938045-08-3

Your foundation for health and self-defense, this is the first English translation of a work considered by the Chinese to be the Bible of T'ai Chi Ch'uan.

Taken from the training notes of T'ai Chi's most famous family, the Yangs, the book gives you detailed advice on breathing techniques, energy generation, meditation, ch'i-kung and much more.

You will appreciate the insightful commentary by Stuart Olson, based on his own extensive experience as a T'ai Chi instructor.

"Chen Kung's book is without question second to none on the subject of T'ai Chi Ch'uan." — **Master T.T. Liang**

"If you are interested in physical immortality, practice yoga, meditate or would like to explore a very ancient, revered and effective way of maintaining physical vitality and youthfulness, you can learn a lot from this book that you would simply never find elsewhere." — **New Age Retailer**

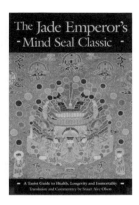

The Jade Emperor's Mind Seal Classic
A Taoist Guide to Health, Longevity and Immortality

Translated by Stuart Alve Olson,
$10.95, paper, 128 pages,
15 illustrations
ISBN 0-938045-10-5

The Taoists believes that there is no reason for a person to ever suffer physical illness. Death itself, whether from old age or sickness, is an unnecessary occurence. Illness and death occur as a result of the dissipation of the Three Treasures - *ching, ch'i and shen* - our reproductive, life-sustaining and spiritual energies. The secret science of restoring, gathering and transforming these primal energies creates an elixir which will confer health, longevity and immortality.

The Jade Emperor's Mind Seal Classic, presented here in the first English translation, is a primer on how to achieve these benefits. A supreme distillation of Taoist thought, the text works as the catalyst for a deep transformation of the being.

Stuart Olson, Taoist practitioner and long-time protege of Taoist and T'ai Chi Ch'uan master, T.T. Liang, provides a lucid translation of, and an insightful commentary on this key text. With its wealth of practical information the commentary will further reward the reader with deeper insights into other great Taoist works, such as *The Secret of the Golden Flower* and *Taoist Yoga: Alchemy and Immortality.*

Olson supplements this classic with a further translation of a rare treatise on *The Three Treasures of Immortality* taken from the Dragon Door sect of Taoism. A collection of aphorisms and quotes from various Taoist scriptures and masters, *The Three Treasures of Immortality*, sheds further light on the processes that will lead you to enhanced health and longevity, if not enlightenment and immortality.

Order Form

Name _____Phone_____

Address _____

City _____State_____ZIP_____

Country _____

Title	Price	Quantity	Total Price
Cultivating the Ch'i	$12.95	_____	_____
Imagination Becomes Reality	$21.95	_____	_____
Jade Emperor	$10.95	_____	_____

Subtotal _____

MN Residents add
6.5% Sales Tax _____

Shipping & Handling ($2.00 for first
book, $0.75 for each additional book.
Double S&H for non-U.S. orders.) _____

Total _____

❏ Check/Money Order Enclosed
❏ VISA   ❏ Mastercard Expires _____

Card # _____

Signature _____

Credit Card orders only: 1-800-247-6553
Dragon Door Publications
P.O. Box 4381, St. Paul, MN 55104
ph. (612)645-0517